Electrons
and
Chemical Bonding

Electrons and Chemical Bonding

Harry B. Gray
Columbia University

1964

W. A. BENJAMIN, INC.   New York   Amsterdam

ELECTRONS AND CHEMICAL BONDING

*The manuscript was put into production on January 16, 1964;
this volume was published on August 21, 1964*

*The publisher is pleased to acknowledge the assistance
of Lenore Stevens, who copyedited the manuscript, and
William Prokos, who produced the illustrations
and designed the dust jacket*

W. A. BENJAMIN, INC.
New York, New York 10016

To my Students in Chemistry 10

Preface

THIS BOOK WAS DEVELOPED from my lectures on chemical bonding in Chemistry 10 at Columbia in the spring of 1962, and is mainly intended for the undergraduate student in chemistry who desires an introduction to the modern theories of chemical bonding. The material is designed for a one-semester course in bonding, but it may have greater use as a supplementary text in the undergraduate chemistry curriculum.

The book starts with a discussion of atomic structure and proceeds to the principal subject of chemical bonding. The material in the first chapter is necessarily quite condensed and is intended as a review. (For more details, the student is referred to R. M. Hochstrasser, *Behavior of Electrons in Atoms*, Benjamin, New York, 1964).

Each chapter in the bonding discussion is devoted to an important family of molecules. Chapters II through VII take up, in order, the principal molecular structures encountered as one proceeds from hydrogen through the second row of the periodic table. Thus, this part of the book discusses bonding in diatomic, linear triatomic, trigonal planar, tetrahedral, trigonal pyramidal, and angular triatomic molecules. Chapters VIII and IX present an introduction to modern ideas of bonding in organic molecules and transition metal complexes. Throughout, our artist has used small dots in drawing the boundary-surface pictures of orbitals. The dots are intended *only* to give a pleasing three-dimensional effect. Our drawings *are not intended* to be charge-cloud pictures. Charge-cloud pictures attempt to show the electronic charge density in an orbital as a function of the distance from the nucleus by varying the "dot concentration."

vii

The discussion of atomic structure does not start with the Schrödinger equation, but with the Bohr theory. I believe most students appreciate the opportunity of learning the development of atomic theory in this century and can make the transition from orbits to orbitals without much difficulty. The student can also calculate several important physical quantities from the simple Bohr theory. At the end of the first chapter, there is a discussion of atomic-term symbols in the Russell-Saunders LSM_LM_S approximation.

In this book the molecular orbital theory is used to describe bonding in molecules. Where appropriate, the general molecular orbitals are compared with valence-bond and crystal-field descriptions. I have written this book for students who have had no training in group theory. Although symmetry *principles* are used throughout in the molecular orbital treatment, the formal group-theoretical methods are not employed, and only in Chapter IX are group-theoretical symbols used. Professor Carl Ballhausen and I are publishing an introductory lecture-note volume on molecular orbital theory, which was written at a slightly higher level than the present book. The lecture notes emphasize the application of group theory to electronic structural problems.

The present material includes problems integrated in the text; most of these are accompanied by the worked-out solutions. There are also a substantial number of problems and questions at the end of each chapter.

It is a great pleasure to acknowledge the unfailing support, encouragement, and devotion of the seventy-seven fellows who took the Columbia College course called Chemistry 10 in the spring of 1962. I doubt if I shall ever have the privilege of working with a finer group. The class notes, written by Stephen Steinig and Robert Price, were of considerable help to me in preparing the first draft.

I would like to thank Professors Ralph G. Pearson, John D. Roberts, and Arlen Viste for reading the manuscript and offering many helpful suggestions. Particularly I wish to thank one of my students, James Halper, who critically read the manuscript in every draft. Finally, a large vote of thanks goes to Diane Celeste, for help above and beyond the call of duty in preparing the final manuscript.

Harry B. Gray

New York
March 1964

Contents

Preface   v

I   Electrons in Atoms   1

    1-1 Introductory Remarks   1
    1-2 Bohr Theory of the Hydrogen Atom (1913)   1
    1-3 The Spectrum of the Hydrogen Atom   5
    1-4 The Need to Modify the Bohr Theory   9
    1-5 Electron Waves   9
    1-6 The Uncertainty Principle   11
    1-7 The Wave Function   12
    1-8 The Schrödinger Wave Equation   13
    1-9 The Normalization Constant   13
    1-10 The Radial Part of the Wave Function   13
    1-11 The Angular Part of the Wave Function   14
    1-12 Orbitals   14
    1-13 Electron Spin   17
    1-14 The Theory of Many-Electron Atoms   20
    1-15 Russell-Saunders Terms   22
    1-16 Ionization Potentials   27
    1-17 Electron Affinities   33

II Diatomic Molecules   36

    2-1 Covalent Bonding   36
    2-2 Molecular-Orbital Theory   38

2–3   Bonding and Antibonding Molecular Orbitals   39
2–4   Molecular-Orbital Energy Levels   42
2–5   The Hydrogen Molecule   46
2–6   Bond Lengths of H_2^+ and H_2 47
2–7   Bond Energies of H_2^+ and H_2 47
2–8   Properties of H_2^+ and H_2 in a Magnetic Field 48
2–9   Second-Row Homonuclear Diatomic Molecules   49
2–10 Other A_2 Molecules   58
2–11 Term Symbols for Linear Molecules   60
2–12 Heteronuclear Diatomic Molecules   62
2–13 Molecular-Orbital Energy-Level Scheme for LiH   67
2–14 Ground State of LiH   68
2–15 Dipole Moments   69
2–16 Electronegativity   69
2–17 Ionic Bonding   73
2–18 Simple Ionic Model for the Alkali Halides   75
2–19 General AB Molecules   78

III   Linear Triatomic Molecules   87

3–1 BeH_2 87
3–2   Energy Levels for BeH_2 89
3–3   Valence-Bond Theory for BeH_2 93
3–4   Linear Triatomic Molecules with π Bonding   95
3–5   Bond Properties of CO_2 100
3–6   Ionic Triatomic Molecules: The Alkaline Earth
      Halides   101

IV   Trigonal-Planar Molecules   106

4–1 BF_3 106
4–2 σ Molecular Orbitals   106
4–3 π Molecular Orbitals   109
4–4   Energy Levels for BF_3 111
4–5   Equivalence of σ_x and σ_y Orbitals 112
4–6   Ground State of BF_3 114
4–7   Valence Bonds for BF_3 115
4–8   Other Trigonal-Planar Molecules   117

V   Tetrahedral Molecules   120

 5–1 CH_4 120
 5–2   Ground State of CH_4 122
 5–3   The Tetrahedral Angle   122
 5–4   Valence Bonds for CH_4 125
 5–5   Other Tetrahedral Molecules   127

VI   Trigonal-Pyramidal Molecules   129

 6–1 NH_3 129
 6–2   Overlap in σ_x, σ_y, and σ_z 130
 6–3   The Interelectronic Repulsions and H—N—H
       Bond Angle in NH_3 135
 6–4   Bond Angles of Other Trigonal-Pyramidal
       Molecules   137
 6–5   Ground State of NH_3 138

VII   Angular Triatomic Molecules   141

 7–1 H_2O 141
 7–2   Ground State of H_2O 143
 7–3   Angular Triatomic Molecules with π Bonding:
       NO_2 148
 7–4 σ Orbitals   148
 7–5 π Orbitals   148
 7–6   Ground State of NO_2 152

VIII   Bonding in Organic Molecules   155

 8–1   Introduction   155
 8–2 C_2H_4 156
 8–3   Energy Levels in C_2H_4 159
 8–4   Ground State of C_2H_4 159
 8–5   Bent-Bond Picture of C_2H_4 160
 8–6   Bond Properties of the C=C Group   162
 8–7   The Value of β_{cc} in C_2H_4 164
 8–8 H_2CO 164
 8–9   Ground State of H_2CO 165

8–10 the $n \rightarrow \pi^*$ Transition Exhibited by the Carbonyl Group 167

8–11 C_2H_2 167

8–12 Ground State of C_2H_2 168

8–13 CH_3CN 168

8–14 C_6H_6 170

8–15 Molecular-Orbital Energies in C_6H_6 171

8–16 Ground State of C_6H_6 173

8–17 Resonance Energy in C_6H_6 173

IX Bonds Involving d Valence Orbitals 176

9–1 Introduction 176

9–2 The Octahedral Complex $Ti(H_2O)_6{}^{3+}$ 176

9–3 Energy Levels in $Ti(H_2O)_6{}^{3+}$ 179

9–4 Ground State of $Ti(H_2O)_6{}^{3+}$ 181

9–5 The Electronic Spectrum of $Ti(H_2O)_6{}^{3+}$ 183

9–6 Valence-Bond Theory for $Ti(H_2O)_6{}^{3+}$ 184

9–7 Crystal-Field Theory for $Ti(H_2O)_6{}^{3+}$ 186

9–8 Relationship of the General Molecular-Orbital Treatment to the Valence-Bond and Crystal-Field Theories 187

9–9 Types of π Bonding in Metal Complexes 188

9–10 Square-Planar Complexes 189

9–11 Tetrahedral Complexes 194

9–12 The Value of Δ 197

9–13 The Magnetic Properties of Complexes: Weak- and Strong-Field Ligands 200

9–14 The Electronic Spectra of Octahedral Cumplexes 201

Suggested Reading 212

Appendix: Atomic Orbital Ionization Energies 215

Index 217

Physical Constants[a]

Planck's constant, h $= 6.6256 \times 10^{-27}$ erg-sec
Velocity of light, c $= 2.997925 \times 10^{10}$ cm sec^{-1}
Electron rest mass, m_e $= 9.1091 \times 10^{-28}$ g
Electronic charge, e $= 4.80298 \times 10^{-10}$ esu (cm $^{3/2}$ sec^{-1})
Bohr radius, a_0 $= 0.529167$ A
Avogadro's number, $N = 6.0247 \times 10^{23}$ mole^{-1} (physical scale)

Conversion Factors

Energy
    1 electron volt (eV) $= 8066$ cm^{-1} $= 23.069$ kcal mole^{-1}
    1 atomic unit (au) $= 27.21$ eV $= 4.3592 \times 10^{-11}$ ergs
      $= 2.1947 \times 10^{5}$ cm^{-1} $= 627.71$ kcal mole^{-1}

Length
    1 Angstrom (A) $= 10^{-8}$ cm

---

[a] Values recommended by the National Bureau of Standards; see *J. Chem. Educ.*, **40**, 642 (1963).

I

Electrons in Atoms

1–1 INTRODUCTORY REMARKS

The main purpose of this book is the discussion of bonding in
several important classes of molecules. Before starting this discussion, we shall review briefly the pertinent details of atomic structure. Since in our opinion the modern theories of atomic structure
began with the ideas of Niels Bohr, we start with the Bohr theory
of the hydrogen atom.

1–2 BOHR THEORY OF THE HYDROGEN ATOM (1913)

Bohr pictured the electron in a hydrogen atom moving in a circular
orbit about the proton (see Fig. 1–1). Note that in Fig. 1–1, m_e represents the mass of the electron, m_n the mass of the nucleus, r the
radius of the circular orbit, and v the linear velocity of the electron.

For a stable orbit, the following condition must be met: the cen-
trifugal force exerted by the moving electron must equal the combined forces of attraction between the nucleus and the electron:

$$\text{centrifugal force} = \frac{m_e v^2}{r} \qquad (1\text{–}1)$$

There are two attractive forces tending to keep the electron in orbit:
the electric force of attraction between the proton and the electron,

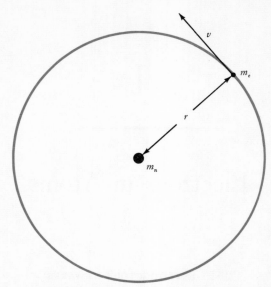

Figure 1–1   Bohr's picture of the hydrogen atom.

and the gravitational force of attraction.   Of these, the electric force greatly predominates and we may neglect the gravitational force:

$$\text{electric force of attraction} = \frac{e^2}{r^2} \tag{1-2}$$

Equating (1–1) and (1–2), we have the condition for a stable orbit, which is

$$\frac{m_e v^2}{r} = \frac{e^2}{r^2} \tag{1-3}$$

We are now able to calculate the energy of an electron moving in one of the Bohr orbits.   The total energy is the sum of the kinetic energy T and the potential energy $V;$ thus

$$E = T + V \tag{1-4}$$

where T is the energy due to motion

$$T = \tfrac{1}{2} m_e v^2 \tag{1-5}$$

and V is the energy due to electric attraction.

$$V = \int_{\infty}^{r} \frac{e^2}{r^2}\, dr = \frac{-e^2}{r} \tag{1-6}$$

Thus the total energy is

$$E = \tfrac{1}{2}m_e v^2 - e^2/r \tag{1-7}$$

However, the condition for a stable orbit is

$$\frac{m_e v^2}{r} = \frac{e^2}{r^2} \quad \text{or} \quad m_e v^2 = \frac{e^2}{r} \tag{1-8}$$

Thus, substituting for $m_e v^2$ in Eq. (1–7), we have

$$E = \frac{1}{2}\frac{e^2}{r} - \frac{e^2}{r} = -\frac{1}{2}\frac{e^2}{r} \tag{1-9}$$

Now we need only specify the orbit radius r and we can calculate the energy. According to Eq. (1–9), all energies are allowed from zero ($r = \infty$) to infinity ($r = 0$).

At this point Bohr made a novel assumption—that *the angular momentum of the system, equal to $m_e vr$, can only have certain discrete values, or quanta.* The result is that only certain electron orbits are allowed. According to the theory, the *quantum unit* of angular momentum is $h/2\pi$ (h is a constant, named after Max Planck, which is defined on page 5). Thus, in mathematical terms, *Bohr's assumption* was

$$m_e vr = n\left(\frac{h}{2\pi}\right) \tag{1-10}$$

with $n = 1, 2, 3 \ldots$ (all integers to ∞). Solving for v in Eq. (1–10), we have

$$v = n\left(\frac{h}{2\pi}\right)\frac{1}{m_e r} \tag{1-11}$$

Substituting the value of v from Eq. (1–11) in the condition for a stable orbit [Eq. (1–8)], we obtain

$$\frac{m_e n^2 h^2}{4\pi^2 m_e^2 r^2} = \frac{e^2}{r} \tag{1-12}$$

or

$$r = \frac{n^2 h^2}{4\pi^2 m_e e^2} \tag{1-13}$$

Equation (1–13) gives the radius of the allowable electron orbits for the hydrogen atom in terms of the *quantum number, n.* The energy associated with each allowable orbit may now be calculated by substituting the value of r from Eq. (1–13) in the energy expression [Eq. (1–9)], giving

$$E = - \frac{2\pi^2 m_e e^4}{n^2 h^2} \tag{1-14}$$

PROBLEMS

1–1. Calculate the radius of the first Bohr orbit.

Solution. The radius of the first Bohr orbit may be obtained directly from Eq. (1–13)

$$r = \frac{n^2 h^2}{4\pi^2 m_e e^2}$$

Substituting $n = 1$ and the values of the constants, we obtain

$$r = \frac{(1)^2 (6.6238 \times 10^{-27} \text{ erg-sec})^2}{4(3.1416)^2 (9.1072 \times 10^{-28} \text{ g})(4.8022 \times 10^{-10} \text{ abs esu})^2}$$
$$= 0.529 \times 10^{-8} \text{ cm} = 0.529 \text{ A}$$

The Bohr radius for $n = 1$ is designated a_0.

1–2. Calculate the velocity of an electron in the first Bohr orbit of the hydrogen atom.

Solution. From Eq. (1–11),

$$v = n\left(\frac{h}{2\pi}\right)\frac{1}{m_e r}$$

Substituting $n = 1$ and $r = a_0 = 0.529 \times 10^{-8}$ cm, we obtain

$$v = (1)\frac{(6.6238 \times 10^{-27} \text{ erg-sec})}{2(3.1416)}$$
$$\times \frac{1}{(9.1072 \times 10^{-28} \text{ g})(0.529 \times 10^{-8} \text{ cm})}$$
$$= 2.188 \times 10^8 \text{ cm sec}^{-1}$$

1-3 THE SPECTRUM OF THE HYDROGEN ATOM

The most stable state of an atom has the lowest energy and this is called the *ground state*. From Eq. (1–14) it is clear that the most stable electronic state of the hydrogen atom occurs when $n = 1$. States that have $n > 1$ are less stable than the ground state and understandably are called *excited states*. The electron in the hydrogen atom may jump from the $n = 1$ level to another n level if the correct amount of energy is supplied. If the energy supplied is light energy, light is absorbed by the atom at the light frequency exactly equivalent to the energy required to perform the *quantum jump*. On the other hand, light is emitted if an electron falls back from a higher n level to the ground-state $(n = 1)$ level.

The light absorbed or emitted at certain characteristic frequencies as a result of the electron changing orbits may be captured as a series of lines on a photographic plate. The lines resulting from light absorption constitute an *absorption spectrum*, and the lines resulting from emission constitute an *emission spectrum*. The frequency v of light absorbed or emitted is related to energy E by the equation deduced by Planck and Einstein,

$$E = hv \qquad (1-15)$$

where h is called Planck's constant and is equal to 6.625×10^{-27} erg-sec.

It was known a long time before the Bohr theory that the positions of the emission lines in the spectrum of the hydrogen atom could be described by a very simple equation

$$v_{\mathrm{H}} = R_{\mathrm{H}}\left(\frac{1}{n^2} - \frac{1}{m^2}\right) \qquad (1-16)$$

where n and m are integers, and where R_{H} is a constant, called the *Rydberg constant* after the man who first discovered the empirical correlation.

This equation can be obtained directly from the Bohr theory as follows: The transition energy (E_{H}) of any electron jump in the hydrogen atom is the energy difference between an initial state I and a final state II. That is,

$$E_{\mathrm{H}} = E_{\mathrm{II}} - E_{\mathrm{I}} \qquad (1-17)$$

or, from Eq. (1–14),

$$E_H = -\frac{2\pi^2 m_e e^4}{n_{II}^2 h^2} - \left(-\frac{2\pi^2 m_e e^4}{n_I^2 h^2}\right) \tag{1-18}$$

$$= \frac{2\pi^2 m_e e^4}{h^2}\left(\frac{1}{n_I^2} - \frac{1}{n_{II}^2}\right) \tag{1-19}$$

Replacing E_H with its equivalent frequency of light from Eq. (1–15), we have

$$\nu_H = \frac{2\pi^2 m_e e^4}{h^3}\left(\frac{1}{n_I^2} - \frac{1}{n_{II}^2}\right) \tag{1-20}$$

Equation (1–20) is equivalent to the experimental result, Eq. (1–16), with $n_I = n$, $n_{II} = m$, and $R_H = (2\pi^2 m_e e^4)/h^3$. Using the value of 9.1085×10^{-28} g for the rest mass of the electron, the Bohr-theory value of the Rydberg constant is

$$R_H = \frac{2\pi^2 m_e e^4}{h^3} = \frac{2(3.1416)^2(9.1085 \times 10^{-28})(4.8029 \times 10^{-10})^4}{(6.6252 \times 10^{-27})^3}$$
$$= 3.2898 \times 10^{15} \text{ cycles/sec} \tag{1-21}$$

It is common practice to express R_H in *wave numbers* $\bar{\nu}$ rather than in frequency. Wave numbers and frequency are related by the equation

$$\nu = c\bar{\nu} \tag{1-22}$$

where c is the velocity of light. Thus

$$R_H = \frac{3.2898 \times 10^{15} \text{ cycles/sec}}{2.9979 \times 10^{10} \text{ cm/sec}} = 109{,}737 \text{ cm}^{-1} \tag{1-23}$$

The accurately known experimental value of R_H is 109,677.581 cm^{-1}. This remarkable agreement of theory and experiment was a great triumph for the Bohr theory.

PROBLEMS

1–3. Calculate the ionization potential of the hydrogen atom. *Solution.* The ionization potential (IP) of an atom or molecule is the energy needed to completely remove an electron from the atom or molecule in its ground state, forming a positive ion. For the hydrogen atom, the process is

$$H \rightarrow H^+ + e \qquad E = IP$$

We may start with Eq. (1–19),

$$E_H = \frac{2\pi^2 m_e e^4}{h^2} \left(\frac{1}{n_I^2} - \frac{1}{n_{II}^2} \right)$$

For the ground state, $n_I = 1$; for the state in which the electron is completely removed from the atom, $n_{II} = \infty$. Thus,

$$IP = \frac{2\pi^2 m_e e^4}{h^2}$$

Recall that

$$a_0 = \frac{h^2}{4\pi^2 m_e e^2}$$

and therefore

$$\frac{1}{2a_0} = \frac{2\pi^2 m_e e^2}{h^2}$$

Then

$$IP = \frac{e^2}{2a_0} = \frac{(4.8022 \times 10^{-10} \text{ abs esu})^2}{2(0.529 \times 10^{-8} \text{ cm})} = 2.179 \times 10^{-11} \text{ erg}$$

Ionization potentials are usually expressed in electron volts. Since 1 erg = 6.2419×10^{11} eV, we calculate

$$IP = 2.179 \times 10^{-11} \text{ erg} = 13.60 \text{ eV}$$

The experimental value of the IP of the hydrogen atom is 13.595 eV.

1–4. Calculate the third ionization potential of the lithium atom.
Solution. The lithium atom is composed of a nucleus of charge $+3(Z = 3)$ and three electrons. The first ionization potential IP_1 of an atom with more than one electron is the energy required to remove one electron; for lithium,

$$Li \rightarrow Li^+ \qquad E = IP_1$$

The energy needed to remove an electron from the unipositive ion Li^+ is defined as the second ionization potential IP_2 of lithium,

$$Li^+ \rightarrow Li^{2+} \qquad E = IP_2$$

and the third ionization potential IP_3 of lithium is therefore the energy required to remove the one remaining electron in Li^{2+}.

The problem of one electron moving around a nucleus of charge $+3$ (or $+Z$) is very similar to the hydrogen atom problem. Since the attractive force is Ze^2/r^2, the condition for a stable orbit is

$$\frac{m_e v^2}{r} = \frac{Ze}{r^2}$$

Carrying this condition through as in the hydrogen atom case and again making the quantum assumption

$$m_e v r = n\left(\frac{h}{2\pi}\right)$$

we find

$$r = \frac{n^2 h^2}{4\pi^2 m_e Z e^2}$$

and

$$E = -\frac{2\pi^2 m_e Z^2 e^4}{n^2 h^2}$$

Thus Eq. (1–19) gives, for the general case of nuclear charge Z,

$$E = \frac{2\pi^2 m_e Z^2 e^4}{h^2}\left(\frac{1}{n_I^2} - \frac{1}{n_{II}^2}\right)$$

or simply $E = Z^2 E_H$. For lithium, $Z = 3$ and $IP_3 = (3)^2(2.179 \times 10^{-11}$ erg$) = 1.961 \times 10^{-10}$ erg $= 122.4$ eV.

1–5. The Lyman series of emission spectral lines arises from transitions in which the excited electron falls back into the $n = 1$ level. Calculate the quantum number n of the initial state for the Lyman line that has $\bar{\nu} = 97{,}492.208$ cm^{-1}.
Solution. We use Eq. (1–20)

$$\nu_H = \frac{2\pi^2 m_e e^4}{h^3}\left(\frac{1}{n_I^2} - \frac{1}{n_{II}^2}\right)$$

in which n_{II} is the quantum number of the initial state for an emission line, and $n_I = 1$ for the Lyman series. Using the experimental value

$$R_H = \frac{2\pi^2 m_e e^4}{ch^3} = 109{,}677.\,581 \text{ cm}^{-1}$$

we have

$$97,492.208 = 109,677.581\left(1 - \frac{1}{n_{II}{}^2}\right) \quad \text{or} \quad n_{II} = 3$$

1-4 THE NEED TO MODIFY THE BOHR THEORY

The idea of an electron circling the nucleus in a well-defined orbit —just as the moon circles the earth—was easy to grasp, and Bohr's theory gained wide acceptance. Little by little, however, it was realized that this simple theory was not the final answer. One difficulty was the fact that an atom in a magnetic field has a more complicated emission spectrum than the same atom in the absence of a magnetic field. This phenomenon is known as the *Zeeman effect* and is not explicable by the simple Bohr theory. However, the German physicist Sommerfeld was able to temporarily rescue the simple theory by suggesting elliptical orbits in addition to circular orbits for the electron. The combined *Bohr-Sommerfeld theory* explained the Zeeman effect very nicely.

More serious was the inability of even the Bohr-Sommerfeld theory to account for the spectral details of the atoms that have several electrons. But these were the 1920s and theoretical physics was enjoying its greatest period. Soon the ideas of de Broglie, Schrödinger, and Heisenberg would put atomic theory on a sound foundation.

1-5 ELECTRON WAVES

In 1924, the French physicist Louis de Broglie suggested that electrons travel in waves, analogous to light waves. The smallest units of light (*light quanta*) are called *photons*. The mass of a photon is given by the Einstein equation of mass-energy equivalence

$$E = mc^2 \qquad (1\text{--}24)$$

Recall from Eq. (1–15) that the energy and frequency of light are related by the expression

$$E = h\nu \qquad (1\text{--}25)$$

Combining Eq. (1–24) and Eq. (1–25), we have

$$m = \frac{h\nu}{c^2} \qquad (1\text{–}26)$$

The momentum p of a photon is

$$p = mv = mc \qquad (1\text{–}27)$$

Substituting the mass of a photon from Eq. (1–26), we have

$$p = \frac{v\nu}{c} \qquad (1\text{–}28)$$

Since frequency ν, wavelength λ, and velocity v are related by the expression

$$\lambda = \frac{v}{\nu} \qquad (1\text{–}29)$$

we find

$$\lambda = \frac{h}{p} \qquad (1\text{–}30)$$

Equation (1–30) gives the wavelength of the light waves or electron waves. For an electron traveling in a circular Bohr orbit, there must be an integral number of wavelengths in order to have a standing wave (see Fig. 1–2), or

$$n\lambda = 2\pi r \qquad (1\text{–}31)$$

Substituting for λ from Eq. (1–30), we have

$$n\left(\frac{h}{p}\right) = 2\pi r$$

or

$$n\left(\frac{h}{2\pi}\right) = rp = \text{angular momentum} \qquad (1\text{–}32)$$

Thus *de Broglie waves* can be used to explain Bohr's novel postulate [Eq. (1–10)].

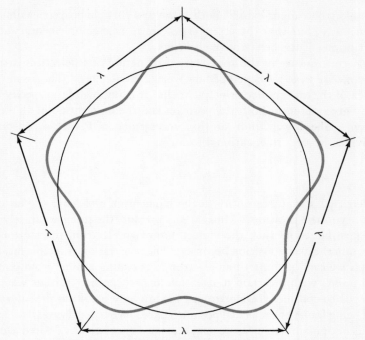

Figure 1–2 A standing electron wave with $n = 5$.

1–6 THE UNCERTAINTY PRINCIPLE

In 1927, Davisson and Germer demonstrated that electrons are diffracted by crystals in a manner similar to the diffraction of X rays. These electron-diffraction experiments substantiated de Broglie's suggestion that an electron has wave properties such as wavelength, frequency, phase, and interference. In seemingly direct contradiction, however, certain other experiments, particularly those of J. J. Thomson, showed that an electron is a particle with mass, energy, and momentum.

As an attempt at an explanation of the above situation, Bohr put forward the *principle of complementarity*, in which he postulated that an electron cannot exhibit both wave and particle properties simultaneously, but that these properties are in fact complementary descriptions of the behavior of electrons.

A consequence of the apparently dual nature of an electron is the *uncertainty principle*, developed by Werner Heisenberg. The essential idea of the uncertainty principle is that it is impossible to specify at any given moment both the position and the momentum of an electron. The lower limit of this uncertainty is Planck's constant divided by 4π. In equational form,

$$(\Delta p_x)(\Delta x) \geq \frac{h}{4\pi} \tag{1-33}$$

Here Δp_x is the uncertainty in the momentum and Δx is the uncertainty in the position. Thus, at any instant, the more accurately it is possible to measure the momentum of an electron, the more uncertain the exact position becomes. The uncertainty principle means that we cannot think of an electron as traveling around from point to point, with a certain momentum at each point. Rather we are forced to consider the electron as having only a certain probability of being found at each fixed point in space. We must also realize that it is not possible to measure simultaneously, and to any desired accuracy, the physical quantities that would allow us to decide whether the electron is a particle or a wave. We thus carry forth the idea that the electron is both a particle and a wave.

1–7   THE WAVE FUNCTION

Since an electron has wave properties, it is described as a wave function, ψ or $\psi(x,y,z)$, the latter meaning that ψ is a function of coordinates x, y, and z. The wave function can take on positive, negative, or imaginary values. The probability of finding an electron in any volume element in space is proportional to the square of the absolute value of the wave function, integrated over that volume of space. This is the physical significance of the wave function. Measurements we make of electronic charge density, then, should be related to $|\psi|^2$, not ψ. Expressed as an equation, we have

$$\text{probability } (x,y,z) \propto |\psi(x,y,z)|^2 \tag{1-34}$$

By way of further explanation, it should be noted that the probability of finding an electron in any volume element must be real and positive, and $|\psi|^2$ always satisfies this requirement.

1–8 THE SCHRÖDINGER WAVE EQUATION

In 1926, the Austrian physicist Erwin Schrödinger presented the equation relating the energy of a system to the wave motion. The *Schrödinger equation* is commonly written in the form

$$\mathcal{H}\psi = E\psi \tag{1-35}$$

where $\mathcal{H}$ is an operator called the Hamiltonian operator (after the English physicist Hamilton) and represents the general form of the kinetic and potential energies of the system; E is the numerical value of the energy for any particular ψ. The wave functions that give solutions to Eq. (1–35) are called *eigenfunctions;* the energies E that result from the solutions are called *eigenvalues*.

The Schrödinger equation is a complicated differential equation and is capable of exact solution only for very simple systems. Fortunately, one of these systems is the hydrogen atom.

The solution of the Schrödinger equation for the hydrogen atom yields wave functions of the general form

$$\psi_{nlm_l} = [N][R_{nl}(r)][\Phi_{lm_l}\left(\frac{x}{r},\frac{y}{r},\frac{z}{r}\right)] \tag{1-36}$$

We shall now attempt to explain the parts of Eq. (1–36).

1–9 THE NORMALIZATION CONSTANT

In Eq. (1–36), N is a *normalization constant*, fixed so that

$$\int_{-\infty}^{\infty}\int_{-\infty}^{\infty}\int_{-\infty}^{\infty} |\psi|^2 \, dx \, dy \, dz = 1 \tag{1-37}$$

That is, the probability of finding the electron somewhere in space must be unity.

1–10 THE RADIAL PART OF THE WAVE FUNCTION

$R_{nl}(r)$ is the *radial part* of the wave function. The value of $|R_{nl}(r)|^2$ gives the probability of finding the electron any distance r

from the nucleus. The two quantum numbers n and l are associated with the radial part of the wave function: n is called the *principal quantum number* and defines the mean radius for the electron; ψ_{nlm_l} can only be an eigenfunction for $n = 1, 2, 3 \ldots$ integers. l is the *quantum number* which specifies the angular momentum of the electron; ψ_{nlm_l} can only be an eigenfunction for $l = 0, 1, 2, 3, \ldots$ to $n - 1$.

1–11   THE ANGULAR PART OF THE WAVE FUNCTION

Φ_{lm_l} $(x/r, y/r, z/r)$ is the *angular part* of the wave function. The quantum numbers l and m_l are associated with the angular part of the wave function. m_l is called the *magnetic quantum number* and defines the possible values for the z-axis component of the angular momentum of the electron in a magnetic field. ψ_{nlm_l} can only be an eigenfunction for $m_l = +l, l - 1, l - 2, \ldots$ to $-l$.

1–12   ORBITALS

The hydrogen eigenfunctions ψ_{nlm_l} are commonly called *orbitals*. The orbitals for the hydrogen atom are classified according to their angular distribution, or l value. Each different l value is assigned a letter:

$l = 0$ is an s orbital.
$l = 1$ is a p orbital.
$l = 2$ is a d orbital.
$l = 3$ is an f orbital.

The letters s, p, d, and f are taken from spectroscopic notation. For $l = 4$ or more, alphabetical order is followed, omitting only the letter j. Thus, $l = 4$ is a g orbital, $l = 5$ is an h orbital, etc.

An orbital is completely specified in this shorthand notation by adding the n and m_l values. The n value goes in front of the letter for the l value. The m_l value is indicated by giving the directional properties of the orbital as a subscript, the total shorthand being

$$nl_{m_l}$$

The complete set of orbitals for hydrogen through $n = 3$ is given in Table 1–1.

Table 1-1

Important Orbitals for the Hydrogen Atom[a]

Orbital quantum numbers			Orbital desig- nation	Radial function,[b] $R_{nl}(r)$	Angular function,[c] $\phi_{lm_l}\left(\frac{x}{r},\frac{y}{r},\frac{z}{r}\right)$
n	l	m_l			
1	0	0	$1s$	$2e^{-r}$	$\dfrac{1}{2\sqrt{\pi}}$
2	0	0	$2s$	$\dfrac{1}{2\sqrt{2}}(2-r)e^{-r/2}$	$\dfrac{1}{2\sqrt{\pi}}$
2	1	$(1)^d$	$2p_x$	$\dfrac{1}{2\sqrt{6}}re^{-r/2}$	$\dfrac{\sqrt{3}\,(x/r)}{2\sqrt{\pi}}$
2	1	0	$2p_z$	$\dfrac{1}{2\sqrt{6}}re^{-r/2}$	$\dfrac{\sqrt{3}\,(z/r)}{2\sqrt{\pi}}$
2	1	$(-1)^d$	$2p_y$	$\dfrac{1}{2\sqrt{6}}re^{-r/2}$	$\dfrac{\sqrt{3}\,(y/r)}{2\sqrt{\pi}}$
3	0	0	$3s$	$\dfrac{2}{81\sqrt{3}}(27-18r+2r^2)e^{-r/3}$	$\dfrac{1}{2\sqrt{\pi}}$
3	1	$(1)^d$	$3p_x$	$\dfrac{4}{81\sqrt{6}}(6r-r^2)e^{-r/3}$	$\dfrac{\sqrt{3}\,(x/r)}{2\sqrt{\pi}}$
3	1	0	$3p_z$	$\dfrac{4}{81\sqrt{6}}(6r-r^2)e^{-r/3}$	$\dfrac{\sqrt{3}\,(z/r)}{2\sqrt{\pi}}$
3	1	$(-1)^d$	$3p_y$	$\dfrac{4}{81\sqrt{6}}(6r-r^2)e^{-r/3}$	$\dfrac{\sqrt{3}\,(y/r)}{2\sqrt{\pi}}$
3	2	$(2)^d$	$3d_{x^2-y^2}$	$\dfrac{4}{81\sqrt{30}}r^2e^{-r/3}$	$\dfrac{\sqrt{15}\,[(x^2-y^2)/r^2]}{4\sqrt{\pi}}$
3	2	$(1)^d$	$3d_{xz}$	$\dfrac{4}{81\sqrt{30}}r^2e^{-r/3}$	$\dfrac{\sqrt{30}\,(xz/r^2)}{2\sqrt{2\pi}}$
3	2	0	$3d_{z^2}$	$\dfrac{4}{81\sqrt{30}}r^2e^{-r/3}$	$\dfrac{\sqrt{5}\,[(3z^2-r^2)/r^2]}{4\sqrt{\pi}}$
3	2	$(-1)^d$	$3d_{yz}$	$\dfrac{4}{81\sqrt{30}}r^2e^{-r/3}$	$\dfrac{\sqrt{30}\,(yz/r^2)}{2\sqrt{2\pi}}$
3	2	$(-2)^d$	$3d_{xy}$	$\dfrac{4}{81\sqrt{30}}r^2e^{-r/3}$	$\dfrac{\sqrt{15}\,(xy/r^2)}{2\sqrt{\pi}}$

[a]Both the radial and the angular functions are normalized to one.

[b]To convert to a general radial function for a one-electron atom with any nuclear charge Z, replace r by Zr/a_0 and multiply each function by $(Z/a_0)^{3/2}$.

[c]Often expressed in the spherical coordinates θ and ϕ by replacing x with $r\sin\theta \times \cos\phi$, y with $r\sin\theta\sin\phi$, and z with $r\cos\theta$.

[d]It is not correct to assign m_l values to the real functions x, y, x^2-y^2, xz, yz, and xy. However, this fiction will help us find the correct terms for linear molecules.

It is common practice to make drawings of the hydrogen orbitals, outlining the region within which there is a large probability for finding the electron. Remember that the electronic density in an orbital is related to the *square of the absolute value of the wave function*. Keep this in mind when you encounter dual-purpose drawings of the boundary surfaces of orbitals, which outline 90 per cent, say, of $|\psi|^2$, and also indicate the $+$ and $-$ signs on the lobes given by the angular part of ψ. The boundary-surface pictures are very useful and should be memorized. The boundary surfaces for s, p, d, and f orbitals are given in Figs. 1–3, 1–4, 1–5, and 1–6, along with radial-distribution graphs for the different orbitals.

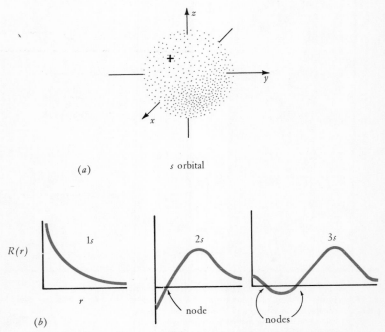

Figure 1–3 (*a*) Boundary surface of an *s* orbital. (*b*) Plots of the radial function $R(r)$ vs. *r* for 1*s*, 2*s*, and 3*s* orbitals. The 2*s* radial function changes sign as *r* increases. Thus there is a point where $R(r) = 0$ for the 2*s* radial function. Such a zero point is called a *node*. The 3*s* radial function has two nodes.

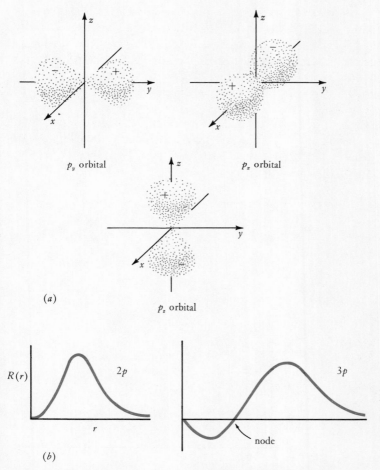

Figure 1–4   (a) Boundary surfaces of the *p* orbitals.   (b) Plots of the radial function $R(r)$ vs. *r* for 2*p* and 3*p* orbitals.   The 3*p* orbital has one node, as indicated.

1–13   ELECTRON SPIN

The three quantum numbers *n*, *l*, and m_l are all associated with the movement of the electron around the nucleus of the hydrogen atom. In order to explain certain precise spectral observations, Goudsmit

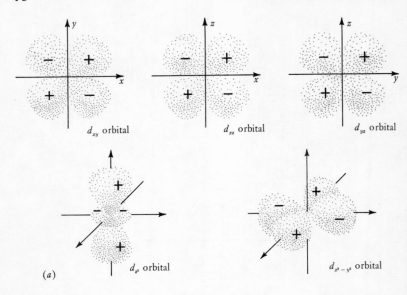

d_{xy} orbital d_{xz} orbital d_{yz} orbital

d_{z^2} orbital $d_{x^2-y^2}$ orbital

(a)

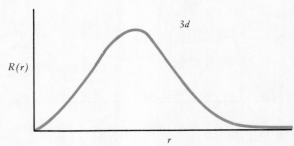

$3d$

$R(r)$

r

(b)

Figure 1–5   (a) Boundary surfaces of the d orbitals.   (b) Plot of $R(r)$ vs. r for a 3d orbital.

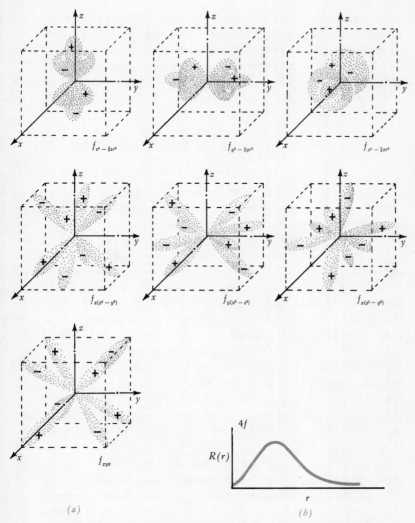

(a)

(b)

Figure 1–6 (a) Boundary surfaces of the f orbitals. (b) Plot of $R(r)$ vs. r for a $4f$ orbital.

and Uhlenbeck (1925) introduced the idea of electron spin (this is analogous to the earth spinning about its own axis while moving in an orbit around the sun). The spin of an electron is quantized in half-integer units, and two more quantum numbers, s and m_s, are added to our collection: s is called the *spin quantum number* and equals $\frac{1}{2}$; m_s is related to s in the same way that m_l is related to l and equals $\pm\frac{1}{2}$.

1–14 THE THEORY OF MANY-ELECTRON ATOMS

It has not been possible to solve the Schrödinger equation exactly for atoms with two or more electrons. Although the orbitals for a many-electron atom are not quite the same as the hydrogen orbitals, we do expect the number of orbitals and their angular dependencies to be the same. Thus the hydrogen orbitals are used to describe the electronic structure of an atom with more than one electron. The procedure is simply to assign to each electron in the atom a set of the four quantum numbers n, l, m_l, and m_s (s is always $\frac{1}{2}$), remembering that *no two electrons can have the same four quantum numbers*. This is a statement of the *Pauli principle*.

What we actually do, then, is to fill up the hydrogen orbitals with the proper number of electrons for the atom under consideration (the *aufbau*, or building up, *principle*). One electron can be placed in each orbital. Since an electron can have m_s equal to $+\frac{1}{2}$ or $-\frac{1}{2}$, two electrons may have the same orbital quantum numbers. The total number of electrons that the different orbital sets can accommodate is given in Table 1–2.

The s, p, d, f, etc., orbital sets usually are called *subshells*. The group of subshells for any given n value is called a *shell*.

The ground-state electronic configuration of a many-electron atom is of greatest interest. In order to determine the ground state of a many-electron atom the orbital sets are filled up in order of increasing energy until all the electrons have been accommodated. We know from experimental observations that the order of increasing energy of the orbital sets in many-electron neutral atoms is $1s$, $2s$, $2p$, $3s$, $3p$, $4s$, $3d$, $4p$, $5s$, $4d$, $5p$, $6s$, $4f$, $5d$, $6p$, $7s$, $5f \frown 6d$. A diagram showing the energies of the orbitals in neutral atoms is given in Fig. 1–7.

Table 1-2
The s, p, d, and f Orbital Sets

Type of orbital	Orbital quantum numbers	Total orbitals in set	Total number of electrons that can be accommodated
s	$l = 0$; $m_l = 0$	1	2
p	$l = 1$; $m_l = 1,0,-1$	3	6
d	$l = 2$; $m_l = 2,1,0,-1,-2$	5	10
f	$l = 3$; $m_l = 3,2,1,0,-1,-2,-3$	7	14

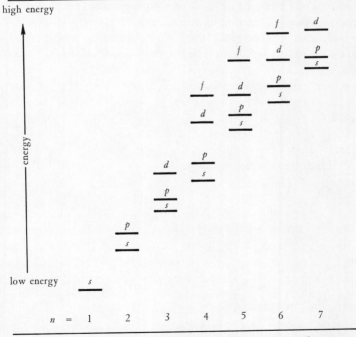

Figure 1-7   Relative energies of the orbitals in neutral atoms.

1-15 RUSSELL-SAUNDERS TERMS

It is convenient to classify an atomic state in terms of total orbital angular momentum L and total spin S (capital letters always are used for systems of electrons; small letters are reserved for individual electrons). This Russell-Saunders LSM_LM_S scheme will now be described in detail.

For a system of n electrons, we define

$$M_L = m_{l_1} + m_{l_2} + m_{l_3} + \cdots + m_{l_n} \qquad (1\text{-}38)$$

$$M_S = m_{s_1} + m_{s_2} + m_{s_3} + \cdots + m_{s_n} \qquad (1\text{-}39)$$

We also have these relationships between L and M_L, S and M_S:

$$M_L = L, L - 1, L - 2, \cdots, -L \qquad (1\text{-}40)$$

$$M_S = S, S - 1, S - 2, \cdots, -S \qquad (1\text{-}41)$$

Let us take the lithium atom as an illustrative example. The *atomic number* (the number of protons or electrons in the neutral atom) of lithium is 3. Therefore the orbital electronic configuration of the ground state is $(1s)^2(2s)^1$. The ground-state LSM_LM_S term is found as follows:

1. Find the possible values of M_L.

$M_L = m_{l_1} + m_{l_2} + m_{l_3}$
$m_{l_1} = m_{l_2} = m_{l_3} = 0$ (all are s electrons)
$M_L = 0$

2. Find the possible values of L.

$M_L = 0$
$L = 0$

3. Find the possible values of M_S.

$M_S = m_{s_1} + m_{s_2} + m_{s_3}$
$m_{s_1} = +\frac{1}{2}, \qquad m_{s_2} = -\frac{1}{2}, \qquad m_{s_3} = \pm\frac{1}{2}$
$M_S = +\frac{1}{2} \quad$ or $\quad -\frac{1}{2}$

4. Find the possible values of S.

$M_S = +\frac{1}{2}, -\frac{1}{2}$
$S = \frac{1}{2}$

A *Russell-Saunders term* is written in the shorthand notation ^{2S+1}L. The superscript $2S + 1$ gives the number of different M_S values of any state, often referred to as the *spin multiplicity*. As in the single-electron-orbital shorthand, letters are used for L. ($L = 0$ is S; $L = 1$ is P; $L = 2$ is D; $L = 3$ is F; etc.) For the lithium atom, the ground-state term has $L = 0$ and $S = \frac{1}{2}$, designated ^2S. An excited electronic configuration for lithium would be $(1s)^2(2p)^1$. For this configuration, we find $M_L = 1, 0, -1(L = 1)$ and $M_S = \pm\frac{1}{2}(S = \frac{1}{2})$. Therefore the term designation of this particular excited state is ^2P.

Admittedly the lithium atom is a very simple case. To find the term designations of the ground state and excited states for more complicated electronic structures, it helps to construct a chart of the possible M_L and M_S values. This more general procedure may be illustrated with the carbon atom. The carbon atom has six electrons. Thus the orbital configuration of the ground state must be $(1s)^2(2s)^2(2p)^2$. It remains for us to find the correct ground-state term.

First a chart is drawn as shown in Fig. 1–8*a*, placing the possible values of M_L in the left-hand column and the possible values of M_S in the top row. We need consider only the electrons in incompletely filled subshells. Filled shells or subshells may be ignored in constructing such a chart since they always give a contribution $M_L = 0(L = 0)$ and $M_S = 0(S = 0)$. (Convince yourself of this before proceeding.) For carbon the configuration $(2p)^2$ is important. Each of the two p electrons has $l = 1$ and can therefore have $m_l = +1, 0,$ or -1. Thus the values possible for M_L range from $+2$ to -2.

Each of the two p electrons can have $m_s = +\frac{1}{2}$ or $-\frac{1}{2}$. Thus the values possible for M_S are 1, 0, and -1.

The next step is to write down all the allowable combinations (called *microstates*) of m_l and m_s values for the two p electrons and to place these microstates in their proper M_L, M_S boxes. The general form for these microstates is

$$\begin{pmatrix} m_{s_1}m_{s_2} \cdots m_{s_n} \\ m_{l_1}m_{l_2} \cdots m_{l_n} \end{pmatrix} \qquad \begin{array}{l} + \text{ stands for } m_s = +\frac{1}{2} \\ - \text{ stands for } m_s = -\frac{1}{2} \end{array}$$

The microstate that fits in the $M_L = 2$, $M_S = 1$ box is $(\overset{+}{1}, \overset{+}{1})$. However, since for both the $2p$ electrons under consideration $n = 2$ and

M_L \ M_S	1	0	−1
2	$(\overset{+}{1},\overset{+}{1})$ Pauli	$(\overset{+}{1},\overset{-}{1})$	
1	$(\overset{+}{1},\overset{+}{0})$	$(\overset{+}{1},\overset{-}{0})$ $(\overset{-}{1},\overset{+}{0})$	$(\overset{-}{1},\overset{-}{0})$
0	$(\overset{+}{1},\overset{+}{-1})$	$(\overset{+}{1},\overset{-}{-1})$ $(\overset{-}{1},\overset{+}{-1})$ $(\overset{+}{0},\overset{-}{0})$	$(\overset{-}{1},\overset{-}{-1})$
−1	$(\overset{+}{-1},\overset{+}{0})$	$(\overset{+}{-1},\overset{-}{0})$ $(\overset{-}{-1},\overset{+}{0})$	$(\overset{-}{-1},\overset{-}{0})$
−2		$(\overset{+}{-1},\overset{-}{-1})$	

(*a*)

M_L \ M_S	1	0	−1
2		$(\overset{+}{1},\overset{-}{1})$	
1	$(\overset{+}{1},\overset{+}{0})$	$(\overset{+}{1},\overset{-}{0})$ $(\overset{-}{1},\overset{+}{0})$	$(\overset{-}{1},\overset{-}{0})$
0	$(\overset{+}{1},\overset{+}{-1})$	$(\overset{+}{1},\overset{-}{-1})$ $(\overset{-}{1},\overset{+}{-1})$ $(\overset{+}{0},\overset{-}{0})$	$(\overset{-}{1},\overset{-}{-1})$
−1	$(\overset{+}{-1},\overset{+}{0})$	$(\overset{+}{-1},\overset{-}{0})$ $(\overset{-}{-1},\overset{+}{0})$	$(\overset{-}{-1},\overset{-}{0})$
−2		$(\overset{+}{-1},\overset{-}{-1})$	

(*b*)

Figure 1-8   (*a*) M_L, M_S microstate chart for the $(2p)^2$ orbital configuration.   (*b*) M_L, M_S microstate chart for the $(2p)^2$ orbital configuration; the ^3P term has been eliminated by crossing out the six microstates in the $M_S = 1$ and $M_S = -1$ columns and, randomly; three microstates with M_L equal to 1, 0, and −1 in the $M_S = 0$ column.

$l = 1$, this microstate is not allowable according to the Pauli principle and is crossed out in Fig. 1-8*a*.

Proceeding to the $M_L = 1$, $M_S = 1$ box, the microstate $(\overset{+}{1}, \overset{+}{0})$ fits and is allowable. The two electrons may both have $m_l = +1$

and therefore $M_L = 2$ if their m_s values differ. Thus the microstate $(\overset{+}{1}, \overline{1})$ is allowable and fits in the $M_L = 2$, $M_S = 0$ box. This procedure is followed until the chart is completed.

From the completed chart the ^{2S+1}L terms may be written down. Start at top left on the chart. There is a microstate with $M_L = 1$, $M_S = 1$. This microstate may be considered the parent of a state that has $L = 1$, $S = 1$, or ^3P. From Eqs. (1–40) and (1–41), we see that a term with $L = 1$ and $S = 1$ has all possible combinations of $M_L = 1,0,-1$ and $M_S = 1,0,-1$. Therefore, a ^3P state must have, in addition to the $M_L = 1$, $M_S = 1$ microstate, microstates with $M_L = 0$, $M_S = 1$; $M_L = -1$, $M_S = 1$; $M_L = 1$, $M_S = 0$; $M_L = 0$, $M_S = 0$; $M_L = -1$, $M_S = 0$; $M_L = 1$, $M_S = -1$; $M_L = 0$, $M_S = -1$; $M_L = -1$, $M_S = -1$. Thus a total of nine microstates are accounted for by the ^3P term. Subtracting these nine microstates from the chart, we are left with a new puzzle, as shown in Fig. 1–8b.

Moving across the top row, there is a microstate with $M_L = 2$, $M_S = 0$, which may be considered the parent of a state that has $L = 2$, $S = 0$, or ^1D. The ^1D state also must have microstates $M_L = 1$, $M_S = 0$; $M_L = 0$, $M_S = 0$; $M_L = -1$, $M_S = 0$; $M_L = -2$, $M_S = 0$. Subtracting these five combinations of the ^1D state, we are left with a single microstate in the $M_L = 0$, $M_S = 0$ box. This microstate indicates that there is a term having $L = 0$, $S = 0$, or ^1S.

We now have the three terms, ^3P, ^1D, and ^1S, which account for all the allowable microstates arising from the $(2p)^2$ electronic configuration. The ground-state term always has maximum spin multiplicity. This is *Hund's first rule*. Therefore, for the carbon atom, the ^3P term is the ground state.

The ^1D and ^1S terms are excited states having the $(2p)^2$ orbital electronic configuration. *Hund's second rule* says that, when comparing two states of the same spin multiplicity, the state with the higher value of L is usually more stable. This is the case with the ^1D and ^1S terms for the carbon atom, since the ^1D state is more stable than the ^1S state.

PROBLEMS

1–6. Work out the ground-state and excited-state terms for the most stable orbital electronic configuration of the titanium atom. *Solution.* The atomic number of titanium is 22. Thus the most stable orbital electronic configuration is $(1s)^2(2s)^2(2p)^6(3s)^2(3p)^6$ $(4s)^2(3d)^2$. The only incompletely filled subshell is $3d$.

Examine Table 1–3, the M_L, M_S chart for the $(3d)^2$ configuration. The $(\overset{+}{2}, \overset{+}{1})$ microstate is the parent of a ^3F term. The ^3F term

Table 1-3
Values of M_L, M_S for $(3d)^2$ Configuration

M_L	M_S 1	M_S 0	M_S −1
4		$(\overset{+}{2},\overset{-}{2})$	
3	$(\overset{+}{2},\overset{+}{1})$	$(\overset{+}{2},\overset{-}{1})(\overset{-}{2},\overset{+}{1})$	$(\overset{-}{2},\overset{-}{1})$
2	$(\overset{+}{2},\overset{+}{0})$	$(\overset{+}{2},\overset{-}{0})(\overset{-}{2},\overset{+}{0})(\overset{+}{1},\overset{-}{1})$	$(\overset{-}{2},\overset{-}{0})$
1	$(\overset{+}{1},\overset{+}{0})(\overset{+}{2},\overset{+}{-1})$	$(\overset{+}{1},\overset{-}{0})(\overset{-}{1},\overset{+}{0})$ $(\overset{+}{2},\overset{-}{-1})(\overset{-}{2},\overset{+}{-1})$	$(\overset{-}{1},\overset{-}{0})(\overset{-}{2},\overset{-}{-1})$
0	$(\overset{+}{2},\overset{+}{-2})(\overset{+}{1},\overset{+}{-1})$	$(\overset{+}{2},\overset{-}{-2})(\overset{-}{2},\overset{+}{-2})$ $(\overset{+}{1},\overset{-}{-1})$ $(\overset{-}{1},\overset{+}{-1})(\overset{+}{0},\overset{-}{0})$	$(\overset{-}{2},\overset{-}{-2})(\overset{-}{1},\overset{-}{-1})$
−1	$(\overset{+}{-1},\overset{+}{0})(\overset{+}{1},\overset{+}{-2})$	$(\overset{+}{-1},\overset{-}{0})(\overset{-}{-1},\overset{+}{0})$ $(\overset{+}{-2},\overset{-}{1})(\overset{-}{-2},\overset{+}{1})$	$(\overset{-}{-1},\overset{-}{0})(\overset{-}{1},\overset{-}{-2})$
−2	$(\overset{+}{-2},\overset{+}{0})$	$(\overset{+}{-2},\overset{-}{0})(\overset{-}{-2},\overset{+}{0})(\overset{+}{-1},\overset{-}{-1})$	$(\overset{-}{-2},\overset{-}{0})$
−3	$(\overset{+}{-2},\overset{+}{-1})$	$(\overset{+}{-2},\overset{-}{-1})(\overset{-}{-2},\overset{+}{-1})$	$(\overset{-}{-2},\overset{-}{-1})$
−4		$(\overset{+}{-2},\overset{-}{-2})$	

accounts for 21 microstates. Starting at the $M_L = 1$, $M_S = 1$ box, there are two microstates. Thus there also must be a ^3P term. The $(\overset{+}{2}, \overset{-}{2})$ microstate is the parent of a ^1G term. The terms ^1D and ^1S account for the remaining microstates in the $M_S = 0$ column.

The ground-state term has maximum spin multiplicity and must be either ^3F or ^3P. The ^3F state has the higher angular momentum $(L = 3)$ and is predicted to be the ground state. The ^3F term is the experimentally observed ground state for the titanium atom. The ^3P state is the first excited state, with the ^1G, ^1D, and ^1S states more unstable.

1-7. Using Table 1–4, work out the terms arising from the orbital electronic configuration $(3d)^1(4d)^1$, and designate the most stable state.

Solution. The $(3d)^1(4d)^1$ problem is slightly different from the $(3d)^2$ problem. Both electrons are d electrons with $l = 2$, but one has $n = 3$ and one has $n = 4$. Thus, for example, the $(\overset{+}{2}, \overset{+}{2})$ microstate does not violate the Pauli principle, since the n quantum numbers differ. The bookkeeping is simplified by adding a subscript 4 to the m_l value for the $4d$ electron.

The terms deduced from the chart for the $(3d)^1(4d)^1$ configuration are ^3G, ^3F, ^3D, ^3P, ^3S, ^1G, ^1F, ^1D, ^1P, and ^1S. Following the spin-multiplicity and angular-momentum rules, the ^3G state should be most stable.

1–16 IONIZATION POTENTIALS

The ionization potential (abbreviated IP) of an atom is the minimum energy required to completely remove an electron from the atom. This process may be written

$$\text{atom} + \text{IP(energy)} \rightarrow \text{unipositive ion} + \text{electron} \quad (1\text{--}42)$$

Further ionizations are possible for all atoms but hydrogen. In general, the ionization energy required to detach the first electron is called IP_1, and subsequent ionizations require IP_2, IP_3, IP_4, etc. Quite obviously, for any atom there are exactly as many IP's as electrons.

The first ionization potentials for most of the atoms are given in Table 1–5. For any atom, the IP_1 is always the smallest IP. This is understandable since removal of a negatively charged particle

Table 1-4
Values of M_L, M_S for $(3d)^1(4d)^1$ Configuration

M_L	M_S		
	1	0	−1
4	$(\overset{+}{2},\overset{+}{2}_4)$	$(\overset{+}{2},\overset{-}{2}_4)(\overset{-}{2},\overset{+}{2}_4)$	$(\overset{-}{2},\overset{-}{2}_4)$
3	$(\overset{+}{2},\overset{+}{1}_4)(\overset{+}{2}_4,\overset{+}{1})$	$(\overset{+}{2},\overset{-}{1}_4)(\overset{-}{2},\overset{+}{1}_4)$ $(\overset{+}{2}_4,\overset{-}{1})(\overset{-}{2}_4,\overset{+}{1})$	$(\overset{-}{2},\overset{-}{1}_4)(\overset{-}{2}_4,\overset{-}{1})$
2	$(\overset{+}{2},\overset{+}{0}_4)(\overset{+}{2}_4,\overset{+}{0})$ $(\overset{+}{1},\overset{+}{1}_4)$	$(\overset{+}{2},\overset{-}{0}_4)(\overset{-}{2},\overset{+}{0}_4)(\overset{+}{2}_4,\overset{-}{0})$ $(\overset{-}{2}_4,\overset{+}{0})(\overset{+}{1},\overset{-}{1}_4)(\overset{-}{1},\overset{+}{1}_4)$	$(\overset{-}{2},\overset{-}{0}_4)(\overset{-}{2}_4,\overset{-}{0})$ $(\overset{-}{1},\overset{-}{1}_4)$
1	$(\overset{+}{1},\overset{+}{0}_4)(\overset{+}{1}_4,\overset{+}{0})$ $(\overset{+}{2},\overset{+}{-1}_4)(\overset{+}{2}_4,\overset{+}{-1})$	$(\overset{+}{1},\overset{-}{0}_4)(\overset{-}{1},\overset{+}{0}_4)(\overset{+}{1}_4,\overset{-}{0})$ $(\overset{-}{1}_4,\overset{+}{0})(\overset{+}{2},\overset{-}{-1}_4)(\overset{-}{2},\overset{+}{-1}_4)$ $(\overset{+}{2}_4,\overset{-}{-1})(\overset{-}{2}_4,\overset{+}{-1})$	$(\overset{-}{1},\overset{-}{0}_4)(\overset{-}{1}_4,\overset{-}{0})$ $(\overset{-}{2},\overset{-}{-1}_4)(\overset{-}{2}_4,\overset{-}{-1})$
0	$(\overset{+}{1},\overset{+}{-1}_4)(\overset{+}{1}_4,\overset{+}{-1})$ $(\overset{+}{2},\overset{+}{-2}_4)(\overset{+}{2}_4,\overset{+}{-2})$ $(\overset{+}{0},\overset{+}{0}_4)$	$(\overset{+}{1},\overset{-}{-1}_4)(\overset{-}{1},\overset{+}{-1}_4)(\overset{+}{1}_4,\overset{-}{-1})$ $(\overset{-}{1}_4,\overset{+}{-1})(\overset{+}{2},\overset{-}{-2}_4)(\overset{-}{2},\overset{+}{-2}_4)$ $(\overset{+}{2}_4,\overset{-}{-2})(\overset{-}{2}_4,\overset{+}{-2})(\overset{+}{0},\overset{-}{0}_4)$	$(\overset{-}{1},\overset{-}{-1}_4)(\overset{-}{1}_4,\overset{-}{-1})$ $(\overset{-}{2},\overset{-}{-2}_4)(\overset{-}{2}_4,\overset{-}{-2})$ $(\overset{-}{0},\overset{-}{0}_4)$
−1	$(\overset{+}{-1},\overset{+}{0}_4)(\overset{+}{-1}_4,\overset{+}{0})$ $(\overset{+}{-2},\overset{+}{1}_4)(\overset{+}{-2}_4,\overset{+}{1})$	$(\overset{+}{-1},\overset{-}{0}_4)(\overset{-}{-1},\overset{+}{0}_4)(\overset{+}{-1}_4,\overset{-}{0})$ $(\overset{-}{-1}_4,\overset{+}{0})(\overset{+}{-2},\overset{-}{1}_4)(\overset{-}{-2},\overset{+}{1}_4)$ $(\overset{+}{-2}_4,\overset{-}{1})(\overset{-}{-2}_4,\overset{+}{1})$	$(\overset{-}{-1},\overset{-}{0}_4)(\overset{-}{-1}_4,\overset{-}{0})$ $(\overset{-}{-2},\overset{-}{1}_4)(\overset{-}{-2}_4,\overset{-}{1})$
−2	$(\overset{+}{-2},\overset{+}{0}_4)(\overset{+}{-2}_4,\overset{+}{0})$ $(\overset{+}{-1},\overset{+}{-1}_4)$	$(\overset{+}{-2},\overset{-}{0}_4)(\overset{-}{-2},\overset{+}{0}_4)(\overset{+}{-2}_4,\overset{-}{0})$ $(\overset{-}{-2}_4,\overset{+}{0})(\overset{+}{-1},\overset{-}{-1}_4)$ $(\overset{-}{-1},\overset{+}{-1}_4)$	$(\overset{-}{-2},\overset{-}{0}_4)(\overset{-}{-2}_4,\overset{-}{0})$ $(\overset{-}{-1},\overset{-}{-1}_4)$
−3	$(\overset{+}{-2},\overset{+}{-1}_4)(\overset{+}{-2}_4,\overset{+}{-1})$	$(\overset{+}{-2},\overset{-}{-1}_4)(\overset{-}{-2},\overset{+}{-1}_4)$ $(\overset{+}{-2}_4,\overset{-}{-1})(\overset{-}{-2}_4,\overset{+}{-1})$	$(\overset{-}{-2},\overset{-}{-1}_4)(\overset{-}{-2}_4,\overset{-}{-1})$
−4	$(\overset{+}{-2},\overset{+}{-2}_4)$	$(\overset{+}{-2},\overset{-}{-2}_4)(\overset{-}{-2},\overset{+}{-2}_4)$	$(\overset{-}{-2},\overset{-}{-2}_4)$

28

Table 1-5

The Electronic Configurations and Ionization Potentials of Atoms

Z	Atom (A)	Orbital electronic configuration	Ground state term	IP_1, eV [a]
1	H	$1s$	^2S	13.595
2	He	$1s^2$	^1S	24.580
3	Li	$[He]2s$	^2S	5.390
4	Be	$[He]2s^2$	^1S	9.320
5	B	$[He]2s^2 2p$	^2P	8.296
6	C	$[He]2s^2 2p^2$	^3P	11.264
7	N	$[He]2s^2 2p^3$	^4S	14.54
8	O	$[He]2s^2 2p^4$	^3P	13.614
9	F	$[He]2s^2 2p^5$	^2P	17.42
10	Ne	$[He]2s^2 2p^6$	^1S	21.559
11	Na	$[Ne]3s$	^2S	5.138
12	Mg	$[Ne]3s^2$	^1S	7.644
13	Al	$[Ne]3s^2 3p$	^2P	5.984
14	Si	$[Ne]3s^2 3p^2$	^3P	8.149
15	P	$[Ne]3s^2 3p^3$	^4S	11.0
16	S	$[Ne]3s^2 3p^4$	^3P	10.357
17	Cl	$[Ne]3s^2 3p^5$	^2P	13.01
18	Ar	$[Ne]3s^2 3p^6$	^1S	15.755
19	K	$[Ar]4s$	^2S	4.339
20	Ca	$[Ar]4s^2$	^1S	6.111
21	Sc	$[Ar]4s^2 3d$	^2D	6.56
22	Ti	$[Ar]4s^2 3d^2$	^3F	6.83
23	V	$[Ar]4s^2 3d^3$	^4F	6.74
24	Cr	$[Ar]4s 3d^5$	^7S	6.763
25	Mn	$[Ar]4s^2 3d^5$	^6S	7.432
26	Fe	$[Ar]4s^2 3d^6$	^5D	7.90
27	Co	$[Ar]4s^2 3d^7$	^4F	7.86
28	Ni	$[Ar]4s^2 3d^8$	^3F	7.633
29	Cu	$[Ar]4s 3d^{10}$	^2S	7.724
30	Zn	$[Ar]4s^2 3d^{10}$	^1S	9.391
31	Ga	$[Ar]4s^2 3d^{10} 4p$	^2P	6.00
32	Ge	$[Ar]4s^2 3d^{10} 4p^2$	^3P	7.88
33	As	$[Ar]4s^2 3d^{10} 4p^3$	^4S	9.81
34	Se	$[Ar]4s^2 3d^{10} 4p^4$	^3P	9.75
35	Br	$[Ar]4s^2 3d^{10} 4p^5$	^2P	11.84

(continued)

Table 1-5 (continued)

Z	Atom (A)	Orbital electronic configuration	Ground state term	IP_1, eV
36	Kr	$[Ar]4s^2\,3d^{10}\,4p^6$	^1S	13.996
37	Rb	$[Kr]5s$	^2S	4.176
38	Sr	$[Kr]5s^2$	^1S	5.692
39	Y	$[Kr]5s^2\,4d$	^2D	6.5
40	Zr	$[Kr]5s^2\,4d^2$	^3F	6.95
41	Nb	$[Kr]5s\,4d^4$	^6D	6.77
42	Mo	$[Kr]5s\,4d^5$	^7S	7.10
43	Tc	$[Kr]5s^2\,4d^5$	^6S	7.28
44	Ru	$[Kr]5s\,4d^7$	^5F	7.364
45	Rh	$[Kr]5s\,4d^8$	^4F	7.46
46	Pd	$[Kr]4d^{10}$	^1S	8.33
47	Ag	$[Kr]5s\,4d^{10}$	^2S	7.574
48	Cd	$[Kr]5s^2\,4d^{10}$	^1S	8.991
49	In	$[Kr]5s^2\,4d^{10}\,5p$	^2P	5.785
50	Sn	$[Kr]5s^2\,4d^{10}\,5p^2$	^3P	7.342
51	Sb	$[Kr]5s^2\,4d^{10}\,5p^3$	^4S	8.639
52	Te	$[Kr]5s^2\,4d^{10}\,5p^4$	^3P	9.01
53	I	$[Kr]5s^2\,4d^{10}\,5p^5$	^2P	10.454
54	Xe	$[Kr]5s^2\,4d^{10}\,5p^6$	^1S	12.127
55	Cs	$[Xe]6s$	^2S	3.893
56	Ba	$[Xe]6s^2$	^1S	5.210
57	La	$[Xe]6s^2\,5d$	^2D	5.61
58	Ce	$[Xe]6s^2\,4f\,5d$	^3H	6.91[b]
59	Pr	$[Xe]6s^2\,4f^3$	^4I	5.76[b]
60	Nd	$[Xe]6s^2\,4f^4$	^5I	6.31[b]
61	Pm	$[Xe]6s^2\,4f^5$	^6H	
62	Sm	$[Xe]6s^2\,4f^6$	^7F	5.6[b]
63	Eu	$[Xe]6s^2\,4f^7$	^8S	5.67[b]
64	Gd	$[Xe]6s^2\,4f^7\,5d$	^9D	6.16[b]
65	Tb	$[Xe]6s^2\,4f^9$?	^6H	6.74[b]
66	Dy	$[Xe]6s^2\,4f^{10}$	^5I	6.82[b]
67	Ho	$[Xe]6s^2\,4f^{11}$	^4I	
68	Er	$[Xe]6s^2\,4f^{12}$	^3H	6.08[c]
69	Tm	$[Xe]6s^2\,4f^{13}$	^2F	5.81[d]
70	Yb	$[Xe]6s^2\,4f^{14}$	^1S	6.2[b]
71	Lu	$[Xe]6s^2\,4f^{14}\,5d$	^2D	5.0[b]
72	Hf	$[Xe]6s^2\,4f^{14}\,5d^2$	^3F	

(continued)

Table 1-5 *(continued)*

Z	Atom (A)	Orbital electronic configuration	Ground state term	IP_1, eV
73	Ta	$[\text{Xe}]6s^2 4f^{14} 5d^3$	^4F	7.88
74	W	$[\text{Xe}]6s^2 4f^{14} 5d^4$	^5D	7.98
75	Re	$[\text{Xe}]6s^2 4f^{14} 5d^5$	^6S	7.87
76	Os	$[\text{Xe}]6s^2 4f^{14} 5d^6$	^5D	8.7
77	Ir	$[\text{Xe}]6s^2 4f^{14} 5d^7$	^4F	9
78	Pt	$[\text{Xe}]6s^2 4f^{14} 5d^9$	^3D	9.0
79	Au	$[\text{Xe}]6s\, 4f^{14} 5d^{10}$	^2S	9.22
80	Hg	$[\text{Xe}]6s^2 4f^{14} 5d^{10}$	^1S	10.43
81	Tl	$[\text{Xe}]6s^2 4f^{14} 5d^{10} 6p$	^2P	6.106
82	Pb	$[\text{Xe}]6s^2 4f^{14} 5d^{10} 6p^2$	^3P	7.415
83	Bi	$[\text{Xe}]6s^2 4f^{14} 5d^{10} 6p^3$	^4S	7.287
84	Po	$[\text{Xe}]6s^2 4f^{14} 5d^{10} 6p^4$	^3P	8.43
85	At	$[\text{Xe}]6s^2 4f^{14} 5d^{10} 6p^5$	^2P	
86	Rn	$[\text{Xe}]6s^2 4f^{14} 5d^{10} 5p^6$	^1S	10.746
87	Fr	$[\text{Rn}]7s$	^2S	
88	Ra	$[\text{Rn}]7s^2$	^1S	5.277
89	Ac	$[\text{Rn}]7s^2 6d$	^2D	
90	Th	$[\text{Rn}]7s^2 6d^2$	^3F	6.95[e]
91	Pa	$[\text{Rn}]7s^2 5f^2 6d$	^4K	
92	U	$[\text{Rn}]7s^2 5f^3 6d$	^5L	6.1[e]
93	Np	$[\text{Rn}]7s^2 5f^4 6d$	^6L	
94	Pu	$[\text{Rn}]7s^2 5f^6$	^7F	5.1[f]
95	Am	$[\text{Rn}]7s^2 5f^7$	^8S	6.0[g]
96	Cm	$[\text{Rn}]7s^2 5f^7 6d$	^9D	
97	Bk	$[\text{Rn}]7s^2 5f^9$	^6H	
98	Cf	$[\text{Rn}]7s^2 5f^{10}$	^5I	
99	Es	$[\text{Rn}]7s^2 5f^{11}$	^4I	
100	Fm	$[\text{Rn}]7s^2 5f^{12}$	^3H	
101	Md	$[\text{Rn}]7s^2 5f^{13}$	^2F	
102	No	$[\text{Rn}]7s^2 5f^{14}$	^1S	
103	Lw	$[\text{Rn}]7s^2 5f^{14} 6d$	^2D	

[a]From C. E. Moore, "Atomic Energy Levels," *NBS Circular 467*, 1949, 1952, and 1958, except as indicated.

[b]T. Moeller, *The Chemistry of the Lanthanides*, Reinhold, New York, 1963, p. 37.

[c]N. I. Ionov and M. A. Mitsev, *Zhur. Eksptl. i Theoret. Fiz.*, **40**, 741 (1961).

[d]J. Blaise and R. Vetter, *Compt. Rend.*, **256**, 630 (1963).

[e]K. F. Zmbov, *Bull. Boris Kidrich Inst. Nucl. Sci.*, **13**, 17 (1962).

[f]R. H. U. M. Dawton and K. L. Wilkinson, *Atomic Energy Research Estab. (Gt. Brit.)*, GR/R, **1906** (1956).

[g]M. Fred and F. S. Tompkins, *J. Opt. Soc. Am.*, **47**, 1076 (1957).

from a neutral atom is easier than its removal from a positively charged ion.

In any column in the periodic table, the IP's decrease as the atomic number increases. Let us examine, for example, the Li and Cs atoms. Lithium, which has $IP_1 = 5.390$ eV, has the electronic configuration [He]$2s$. Cesium, with $IP_1 = 3.893$ eV, has the structure [Xe]$6s$. The $2s$ electron in Li spends much more time near the nucleus than the $6s$ electron does in Cs. This means that the *effective nuclear charge* Z_{eff} felt by the $2s$ electron in Li is considerably larger than the Z_{eff} felt by the $6s$ electron in Cs, a fact that is illustrated in Fig. 1–9.

In any row in the periodic table, the IP's generally increase from left to right, being smallest for the alkali metal atoms and largest for the inert gas atoms. There are irregularities, however, since atoms

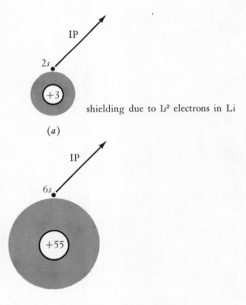

IP

$2s$

$+3$

shielding due to $1s^2$ electrons in Li

(*a*)

IP

$6s$

$+55$

shielding due to $1s^2 2s^2 2p^6 3s^2 3p^6 4s^2 3d^{10} 4p^6 5s^2 4d^{10} 5p^6$ electrons

(*b*)

Figure 1–9   Ionization of an electron from (*a*) a lithium atom and (*b*) a cesium atom.

with filled or half-filled subshells have larger IP's than might be expected. For example, Be($[He]2s^2$) has $IP_1 = 9.320$ eV and B($[He]2s^22p^1$) has $IP_1 = 8.296$ eV; N($[He]2s^22p^3$) has $IP_1 = 14.54$ eV and O($[He]2s^22p^4$) has $IP_1 = 13.614$ eV. The steady if slightly irregular increase in IP's from Li ($IP_1 = 5.390$ eV) to Ne ($IP_1 = 21.559$ eV) is due to the steady increase in Z_{eff} observed between Li and Ne. The electrons added from Li to Ne all enter $2s$ and $2p$ orbitals and are not able to completely shield each other from the increasing nuclear charge.

The variation of the ionization potential of atoms with atomic number is shown in Fig. 1–10.

1–17 ELECTRON AFFINITIES .

The electron affinity (abbreviated EA) of an atom is the energy released (or needed, if the atom has a negative EA) when the atom

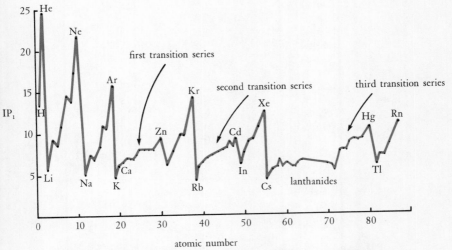

Figure 1–10 **Variation of atomic ionization potential with atomic number.**

adds an extra electron to give a negative ion. Thus we have' the equation

$$\text{atom} + \text{electron} \rightarrow \text{uninegative ion} + \text{EA(energy)} \quad (1\text{–}43)$$

Table 1-6

Atomic Electron Affinities

Atom (A)	Orbital electronic configuration	EA, eV	Orbital electronic configuration of A⁻
H	$1s$	0.747^{a}	He
F	$[He]2s^2 2p^5$	3.45^{b}	Ne
Cl	$[Ne]3s^2 3p^5$	3.61^{b}	Ar
Br	$[Ar]4s^2 3d^{10} 4p^5$	3.36^{b}	Kr
I	$[Kr]5s^2 4d^{10} 5p^5$	3.06^{b}	Xe
O	$[He]2s^2 2p^4$	1.47^{c}	$[He]2s^2 2p^5$
S	$[Ne]3s^2 3p^4$	2.07^{d}	$[Ne]3s^2 3p^5$
Se	$[Ar]4s^2 3d^{10} 4p^4$	$(1.7)^{e}$	$[Ar]4s^2 3d^{10} 4p^5$
Te	$[Kr]5s^2 4d^{10} 5p^4$	$(2.2)^{e}$	$[Kr]5s^2 4d^{10} 5p^5$
N	$[He]2s^2 2p^3$	$(-0.1)^{f}$	$[He]2s^2 2p^4$
P	$[Ne]3s^2 3p^3$	$(0.7)^{f}$	$[Ne]3s^2 3p^4$
As	$[Ar]4s^2 3d^{10} 4p^3$	$(0.6)^{f}$	$[Ar]4s^2 3d^{10} 4p^4$
C	$[He]2s^2 2p^2$	1.25^{g}	$[He]2s^2 2p^3$
Si	$[Ne]3s^2 3p^2$	$(1.63)^{f}$	$[Ne]3s^2 3p^3$
Ge	$[Ar]4s^2 3d^{10} 4p^2$	$(1.2)^{f}$	$[Ar]4s^2 3d^{10} 4p^3$
B	$[He]2s^2 2p$	$(0.2)^{a}$	$[He]2s^2 2p^2$
Al	$[Ne]3s^2 3p$	$(0.6)^{a}$	$[Ne]3s^2 3p^2$
Ga	$[Ar]4s^2 3d^{10} 4p$	$(0.18)^{f}$	$[Ar]4s^2 3d^{10} 4p^2$
In	$[Kr]5s^2 4d^{10} 5p$	$(0.2)^{f}$	$[Kr]5s^2 4d^{10} 5p^2$
Be	$[He]2s^2$	$(-0.6)^{a}$	$[He]2s^2 2p$
Mg	$[Ne]3s^2$	$(-0.3)^{a}$	$[Ne]3s^2 3p$
Li	$[He]2s$	$(0.54)^{a}$	$[He]2s^2$
Na	$[Ne]3s$	$(0.74)^{a}$	$[Ne]3s^2$
Zn	$[Ar]4s^2 3d^{10}$	$(-0.9)^{f}$	$[Ar]4s^2 3d^{10} 4p$
Cd	$[Kr]5s^2 4d^{10}$	$(-0.6)^{f}$	$[Kr]5s^2 4d^{10} 5p$

[a] H. A. Skinner and H. O. Pritchard, *Trans. Faraday Soc.*, **49**, 1254 (1953).
[b] R. S. Berry and C. W. Riemann, *J. Chem. Phys.*, **38**, 1540 (1963).
[c] L. M. Branscomb, *Nature*, **182**, 248 (1958).
[d] L. M. Branscomb and S. J. Smith, *J. Chem. Phys.*, **25**, 598 (1956).
[e] H. O. Pritchard, *Chem. Revs.*, **52**, 529 (1953).
[f] A. P. Ginsburg and J. M. Miller, *J. Inorg. Nucl. Chem.*, **7**, 351 (1958).
[g] M. L. Seman and L. M. Branscomb, *Phys. Rev.*, **125**, 1602 (1962).

Unfortunately, as a result of certain experimental difficulties, very few EA values are precisely known. A representative list is given in Table 1–6.

The halogen atoms have relatively large EA's, since the resulting halide ions have a stable filled-shell electronic configuration. Atoms with filled subshells often have negative EA values. Good examples are Be, Mg, and Zn.

It is interesting to note that the atoms in the nitrogen family, with the electronic configuration $s^2p^3(^4S)$, have very small EA's. Thus we have additional evidence for the greater stability of a half-filled subshell.

SUPPLEMENTARY PROBLEMS

1(a). Compare the velocity and radius of an electron in the fourth Bohr orbit with the velocity and radius of an electron in the first Bohr orbit; (b) Derive the expression, dependent only on the variable n, for the velocity of an electron in a Bohr orbit.

2. Calculate the energy of an electron in the Bohr orbit with $n = 3$.

3. Calculate the second ionization potential of He.

4. Calculate the frequencies of the first three lines in the Lyman series (the lowest-frequency lines).

5. The Balmer series in the spectrum of the hydrogen atom arises from transitions from higher levels to $n = 2$. Find which of the Balmer lines fall in the visible region of the spectrum (visible light wavelengths are between 4000 and 7000 A).

6. Following the Pauli principle and Hund's first rule, give the orbital configuration and the number of unpaired electrons in the ground state for the following atoms: (a) N; (b) S; (c) Ca; (d) Fe; (e) Br.

7. Find the terms for the following orbital configurations, and in each case designate the term of lowest energy: (a) $2s$; (b) $2p^3$; (c) $2p^23s$; (d) $2p3p$; (e) $2p3d$; (f) $3d^3$; (g) $3d^5$; (h) $3d^9$; (i) $2s4f$; (j) $2p^5$; (k) $3d^34s$.

8. Find the ground-state term for the following atoms: (a) Si; (b) Mn; (c) Rb; (d) Ni.

II

Diatomic Molecules

2–1 COVALENT BONDING

A molecule is any stable combination of more than one atom. The simplest neutral molecule is a combination of two hydrogen atoms, which we call the hydrogen molecule or H_2. The H_2 molecule is *homonuclear*, since both atomic nuclei used in forming the molecule are the same.

The forces that hold two hydrogen atoms together in the H_2 molecule are described collectively by the word *bond*. We know this bond to be quite strong, since at ordinary temperatures hydrogen exists in the form H_2, not H atoms. Only at very high temperatures is H_2 broken up into its H atom components. Let us try to visualize the bonding in H_2 by allowing two hydrogen atoms to approach each other, as illustrated in Fig. 2–1. When the atoms are at close range, two electrostatic forces become important: first, the attraction between the nucleus H_a and the electron associated with $1s_b$, as well as that between the nucleus H_b and the electron associated with $1s_a$; and second, the repulsion between H_a and H_b as well as that between $1s_a$ and $1s_b$.

The attractive term is more important at large H_a–H_b distances, but the situation changes as the two atoms come closer together, the importance of the H_a–H_b repulsion increasing as internuclear distances become very short. This state of affairs is described by an

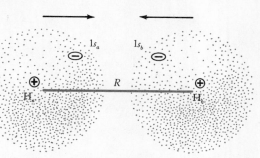

Figure 2-1   Schematic drawing of two hydrogen atoms approaching each other.

energy curve such as that shown in Fig. 2–2. The energy of the system falls until the H_a–H_b repulsion at very short ranges forces the energy back up again. The minimum in the curve gives both *the most stable internuclear separation in the H_2 molecule* and *its gain in stability over two isolated H atoms.*

One of the early successful pictures of a chemical bond involving electrons and nuclei resulted from the work of the American physical chemist, G. N. Lewis. Lewis formulated the electron-pair bond, in which the combining atoms tend to associate themselves with just enough electrons to achieve an inert-gas electronic configuration. The hydrogen molecule is, in the Lewis theory, held together by an electron-pair bond (Fig. 2–3). Each hydrogen has the same partial claim to the electron pair and thus achieves the stable $1s^2$ helium configuration. A bond in which the electrons are equally shared by the participating nuclei is called a *covalent bond.*

The remainder of this book will be devoted to the modern ideas of bonding in several important classes of molecules. The emphasis will be on the molecular-orbital theory, with comparisons made from time to time to the valence-bond theory. Of the many scientists involved in the development of these theories, the names of R. S. Mulliken (molecular-orbital theory) and Linus Pauling (valence-bond theory) are particularly outstanding.

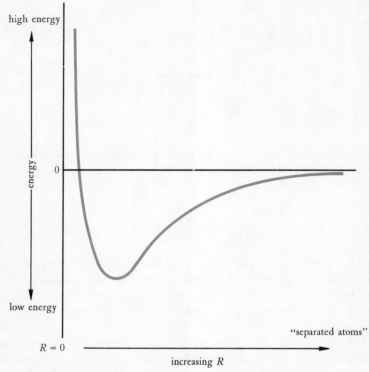

Figure 2–2 Energy of a system of two hydrogen atoms as a function of internuclear separation.

2–2 MOLECULAR-ORBITAL THEORY

According to molecular-orbital theory, electrons in molecules are in orbitals that may be associated with several nuclei. *Molecular orbitals* in their simplest approximate form are considered to be *linear combinations of atomic orbitals*. We assume that when an electron in a molecule is near one particular nucleus, the molecular wave function is approximately an atomic orbital centered at that nucleus. This means that we can form molecular orbitals by simply adding and subtracting appropriate atomic orbitals. The method is usually abbreviated LCAO–MO, which stands for *linear combination of atomic*

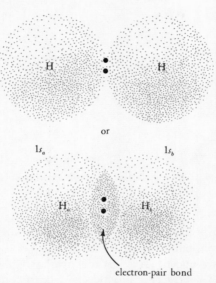

Figure 2–3   Electron-pair bond in the hydrogen molecule.

orbitals–molecular orbitals.   We shall use the abbreviation MO in this text for a molecular orbital.

Atomic orbitals that are in the proper stability range to be used in bonding are called *valence orbitals.*   The valence orbitals of an atom are those that have accepted electrons since the last inert gas and, in addition, any others in the stability range of the orbitals that will be encountered before the next inert gas.   For example, the valence orbital of the hydrogen atom is $1s$.   The $2s$ and $2p$ orbitals of hydrogen are too high in energy to be used in strong bonding.

2–3   BONDING AND ANTIBONDING MOLECULAR ORBITALS

Let us consider now the MO bonding scheme for the simplest imaginable molecule, one with two protons and one electron.   This combination is H_2^+, the hydrogen molecule-ion.   Each hydrogen in

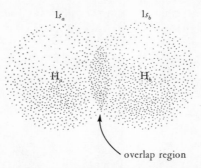

Figure 2–4   The overlap of two hydrogen 1s orbitals in H_2^+.

the molecule has a 1s valence orbital, as shown in Fig. 2–4. Notice that the two atomic orbitals *overlap* in the heavily shaded region between the two nuclei. It is just this overlap region that is affected by adding and subtracting atomic orbitals to construct molecular orbitals.

There are two different ways in which we can linearly combine two 1s hydrogen atomic orbitals. The first is to add them together (Fig. 2–5). It is easy to see from this figure that an electron in MO I will spend most of its time in the overlap region between the nuclei H_a and H_b. This maximizes the attractive force between the electron and the two nuclei; therefore an electron in this MO is *more*

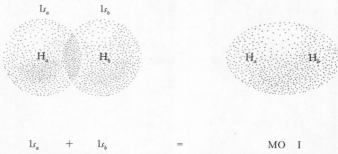

$1s_a$ + $1s_b$ =   MO   I

Figure 2–5   Schematic drawing of the formation of the bonding MO of H_2^+.

stable than in either isolated $1s$ atomic orbital. We refer to such an MO as *bonding*. Furthermore, this MO is symmetric for rotation about a line joining the two H nuclei. That is, if we place an arrow through the two nuclei, and then turn the arrow, the MO still looks exactly the same (Fig. 2–6). We call an orbital with such *cylindrical symmetry* a σ *molecular orbital*.[1] The σ bonding MO will be abbreviated σ^b.

The other linear combination is formed by subtraction of one of the two hydrogen $1s$ orbitals from the other (Fig. 2–7). This type of MO has a node in the region between the two nuclei. Thus an electron in MO II will never be found halfway between the two nuclei; instead it will be mainly confined to space outside the overlap region. An electron in MO II is less stable than in an isolated $1s$ hydrogen atomic orbital, and we therefore say that II is *antibonding*. The antibonding MO also has cylindrical symmetry and thus is σ antibonding or σ*.

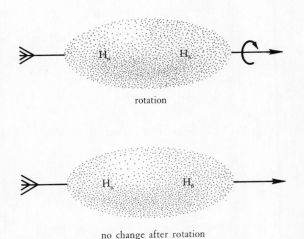

rotation

no change after rotation

Figure 2–6   Rotation of the bonding MO of H_2^+ about the internuclear axis.

---

[1] In fact, any molecular orbital that does not have a nodal plane *containing* the internuclear axis is a σ molecular orbital.

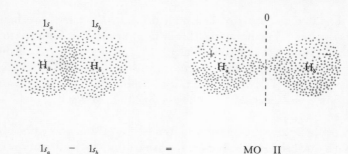

$1s_a \quad - \quad 1s_b \qquad\qquad = \qquad\qquad$ MO II

Figure 2–7   Schematic drawing of the formation of the antibonding MO of H_2^+.

2–4   MOLECULAR-ORBITAL ENERGY LEVELS

The approximate wave functions for the σ^b and σ^* molecular orbitals are:

$$\psi(\sigma^b) = N^b(1s_a + 1s_b) \qquad (2-1)$$

$$\psi(\sigma^*) = N^*(1s_a - 1s_b) \qquad (2-2)$$

Equations (2–1) and (2–2) are simply the analytical expressions for the molecular orbitals shown in Figs. 2–5 and 2–7, respectively. The values of the constants N^b and N^* in Eqs. (2–1) and (2–2) are fixed by the normalization condition,

$$\int |\psi|^2 \, dx \, dy \, dz = \int |\psi|^2 \, d\tau = 1 \qquad (2-3)$$

Let us proceed to evaluate N^b.   First we substitute $\psi(\sigma^b)$ in Eq. (2–3), giving

$$\begin{aligned}
\int [\psi(\sigma^b)]^2 \, d\tau = 1 &= \int [N^b(1s_a + 1s_b)]^2 \, d\tau \\
&= (N^b)^2 [\int (1s_a)^2 \, d\tau + \int (1s_b)^2 \, d\tau \\
&\qquad\qquad + 2\int (1s_a)(1s_b) \, d\tau] \qquad (2-4)
\end{aligned}$$

Provided the atomic orbitals $1s_a$ and $1s_b$ are already normalized,

$$\int (1s_a)(1s_a) \, d\tau = \int (1s_b)(1s_b) \, d\tau = 1 \qquad (2-5)$$

The integral involving both $1s_a$ and $1s_b$ is called the *overlap integral* and is denoted by the letter S:

$$S = \text{overlap integral} = \int (1s_a)(1s_b) \, d\tau \qquad (2-6)$$

Thus, Eq. (2–4) reduces to

$$(N^b)^2[2 + 2S] = 1 \tag{2–7}$$

and

$$N^b = \pm\sqrt{\frac{1}{2(1 + S)}} \tag{2–8}$$

In our approximate scheme we shall neglect the overlap integral in determining the normalization constant.[1] Therefore, arbitrarily picking the positive sign in Eq. (2–8), we have

$$N^b = \sqrt{\tfrac{1}{2}} \tag{2–9}$$

The value of N^* is obtained in the same fashion, by substituting Eq. (2–2) in Eq. (2–3) and solving for N^*. The result is

$$N^* = \pm\sqrt{\frac{1}{2(1 - S)}} \tag{2–10}$$

or, with the $S = 0$ approximation,

$$N^* = \sqrt{\tfrac{1}{2}} \tag{2–11}$$

The approximate molecular orbitals for H_2^+ are therefore

$$\psi(\sigma^b) = \frac{1}{\sqrt{2}}(1s_a + 1s_b) \tag{2–12}$$

$$\psi(\sigma^*) = \frac{1}{\sqrt{2}}(1s_a - 1s_b) \tag{2–13}$$

The energies of these molecular orbitals are obtained from the Schrödinger equation,

$$\mathcal{H}\psi = E\psi \tag{2–14}$$

Multiplying both sides of Eq. (2–14) by ψ and then integrating, we have

$$\int \psi \mathcal{H}\psi \, d\tau = E\int \psi^2 \, d\tau \tag{2–15}$$

---

[1] This approximation involves a fairly substantial error in the case of H_2^+. The overlap of $1s_a$ and $1s_b$ in H_2^+ is 0.590. Thus we calculate $N^b = 0.560$, as compared to $N^b = 0.707$ for the $S = 0$ approximation. In most other cases, however, the overlaps are smaller (usually between 0.2 and 0.3) and the approximation involves only a small error.

Since $\int \psi^2 \, d\tau = 1$, Eq. (2–15) reduces to

$$E = \int \psi \mathcal{H} \psi \, d\tau \qquad (2\text{–}16)$$

Substituting Eq. (2–12) in Eq. (2–16), we have

$$
\begin{aligned}
E[\psi(\sigma^b)] &= \int [\psi(\sigma^b)]\mathcal{H}[\psi(\sigma^b)] \, d\tau = \tfrac{1}{2}\int (1s_a + 1s_b)\mathcal{H}(1s_a + 1s_b) \, d\tau \\
&= \tfrac{1}{2}\int (1s_a)\mathcal{H}(1s_a) \, d\tau + \tfrac{1}{2}\int (1s_b)\mathcal{H}(1s_b) \, d\tau \\
&\quad + \tfrac{1}{2}\int (1s_a)\mathcal{H}(1s_b) \, d\tau + \tfrac{1}{2}\int (1s_b)\mathcal{H}(1s_b) \, d\tau \qquad (2\text{–}17)
\end{aligned}
$$

We shall not attempt to evaluate the various integrals in Eq. (2–17), but instead shall replace them using the following shorthand:

$$q_a = \int (1s_a)\mathcal{H}(1s_a) \, d\tau \qquad (2\text{–}18)$$

$$q_b = \int (1s_b)\mathcal{H}(1s_b) \, d\tau \qquad (2\text{–}19)$$

$$\beta = \int (1s_a)\mathcal{H}(1s_b) \, d\tau = \int (1s_b)\mathcal{H}(1s_a) \, d\tau \qquad (2\text{–}20)$$

In this case, since $1s_a$ and $1s_b$ are equivalent atomic orbitals,

$$q_a = q_b = q \qquad (2\text{–}21)$$

We shall call q_a and q_b *coulomb integrals*. The coulomb integral represents the energy required to remove an electron from the valence orbital in question, in the field of the nuclei and other electrons in the molecule. Thus it is sometimes referred to as a *valence ionization potential*.

We shall call β the *exchange integral* in this text. In other sources, however, you may find β referred to as a *resonance* or *covalent integral*. We have seen that an electron in the σ^b molecular orbital spends most of its time in the overlap region common to both nuclei. Thus the electron is stabilized in this favorable position for nucleus a–electron–nucleus b attractions. The exchange integral β simply represents this added covalent-bonding stability.

Simplifying Eq. (2–17), we have finally

$$E[\psi(\sigma^b)] = q + \beta \qquad (2\text{–}22)$$

The energy of the σ^* molecular orbital is found in the same manner, substitution in Eq. (2–16) giving

$$E[\psi(\sigma^*)] = \tfrac{1}{2}\int (1s_a - 1s_b)\mathcal{H}(1s_a - 1s_b) \, d\tau = q - \beta \qquad (2\text{–}23)$$

This result shows that the antibonding molecular orbital is less stable than the bonding molecular orbital by an amount equal to -2β. An electron in the σ^* molecular orbital has only a small probability of being found in the energetically favored overlap region. Instead it is confined to the extreme ends of the molecule, which are positions of high energy relative to the middle of the molecule.

It is convenient to show the relative molecular-orbital energies in a diagram. Such a diagram for H_2^+ is shown in Fig. 2–8. The valence orbitals of the combining atoms are represented in the outside columns and are ordered in terms of their *coulomb energy*. The most stable valence orbitals are placed lowest in the diagram. Since $1s_a$ and $1s_b$ have the same coulomb energy, these levels are placed directly opposite one another.

The molecular-orbital energies are indicated in the middle column. The σ^b orbital is shown to be more stable than the combining $1s$ valence orbitals, and the σ^* orbital is shown to be correspondingly less stable.

The electron in the ground state of H_2^+ occupies the more stable molecular orbital; that is,

$$\text{ground state of } H_2^+ = \sigma^b$$

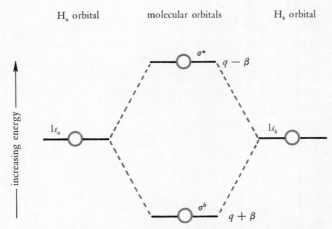

Figure 2–8 **Relative molecular-orbital energies for H_2^+.**

PROBLEM

2–1. Calculate the energies of the σ^b and σ^* orbitals for H_2^+, including the overlap integral S. Show that σ^* is destabilized more than σ^b is stabilized if the overlap is different from zero.

2–5   THE HYDROGEN MOLECULE

The orbital electronic structures of molecules with more than one valence electron are built up by placing the valence electrons in the most stable molecular orbitals appropriate for the valence orbitals of the nuclei in the molecule. We have constructed the molecular orbitals for the system of two protons and two $1s$ atomic orbitals. This set of orbitals is appropriate for H_2^+, H_2, H_2^-, etc. The hydrogen molecule, H_2, has two electrons that can be placed in the molecular orbitals given in the energy-level diagram (Fig. 2–8). Both electrons can be placed in the σ^b level, provided they have different spin (m_s) quantum numbers (the Pauli principle). Thus we represent the ground state of H_2

ground state of $H_2 = (\sigma^b)^2$ or $[\sigma^b(m_s = +\frac{1}{2})][\sigma^b(m_s = -\frac{1}{2})]$

which is our shorthand is $(\overset{+}{\sigma}{}^b)(\overset{-}{\sigma}{}^b)$.

This picture of the bond in H_2 involving two electrons, each in a σ^b orbital but with opposite spins, is analogous to the Lewis electron-pair bond in H_2 (Fig. 2–3). It is convenient to carry along the idea that a full bond between any two atoms involves two electrons. Thus we define as a useful theoretical quantity the number of bonds in a molecule as follows:

$$\text{number of bonds} = \frac{\begin{array}{c}(\text{number of electrons in bonding MO's}) - \\ (\text{number of electrons in antibonding MO's})\end{array}}{2}$$

$$(2\text{–}24)$$

One electron in an antibonding MO is considered to cancel out the bonding stability imparted by one electron in a bonding MO. Using this formula we see that H_2^+ has half a σ bond and H_2 has one σ bond.

2–6 BOND LENGTHS OF H_2^+ AND H_2

A useful experimental quantity reflecting electronic structure is *bond length*. The *standard bond length* for a bond between any two atoms is the *equilibrium internuclear separation*.[1] We shall express this distance between nuclei in Angstrom units and refer to it as R. The bond lengths of H_2^+ and H_2 in the ground state are 1.06 and 0.74 A, respectively, as shown in Fig. 2–9. Thus the H_2 molecule, with one σ bond, has a shorter R than does H_2^+, with only half a σ bond. In general, when molecules with nuclei of approximately the same atomic number are compared, the bond length is shortest between the two atoms with the largest number of bonds.

2–7 BOND ENERGIES OF H_2^+ AND H_2

Another useful experimental quantity that reflects electronic structure is *bond-dissociation energy*. The *standard bond-dissociation energy*

$$\left(H \underline{\hspace{2cm}}^{R\ =\ 1.06A} H \right)^+ \qquad \tfrac{1}{2}\ \sigma\text{-bond}$$

$$H \underline{\hspace{2cm}}^{R\ =\ 0.74A} H \qquad 1\ \sigma\text{-bond}$$

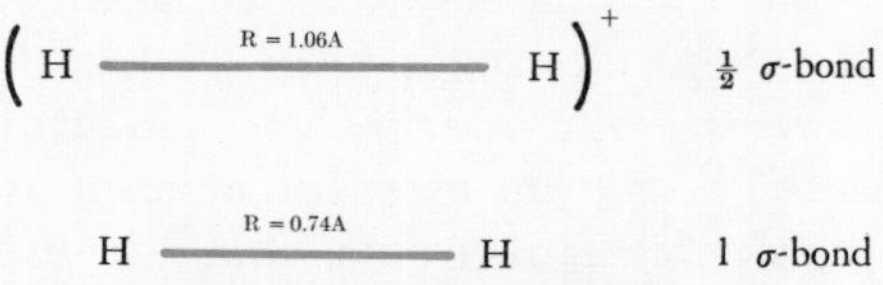

Figure 2–9 Comparison of H_2^+ and H_2.

---

[1] To make matters more complicated for us, nuclei in molecules are always vibrating. For example, the bond in H_2, say, stretches and contracts as shown schematically below:

contracting
←————
H-H ⟷ H—H ⟷ H——H
contracted   equilibrium   stretched
internuclear
separation
————→
stretching

The equilibrium internuclear separation about which the nuclei vibrate is the standard bond length.

for a bond between any two atoms is the *energy required to break the bond, giving isolated ground-state atoms;* i.e.,

$$H_2 + \text{bond-dissociation energy} \rightarrow H + H \qquad (2\text{-}25)$$

We shall express bond energy in kcal/mole units, and refer to a particular bond energy as DE (atom 1–atom 2). The bond energies of H_2^+ and H_2 are 61.06 and 103.24 kcal/mole, respectively. We see that H_2, with one σ bond, has a larger bond energy than H_2^+. This is again a very general result, since bond energies in an analogous series of molecules increase with an increasing number of bonds.

2–8   PROPERTIES OF H_2^+ AND H_2 IN A MAGNETIC FIELD

Most substances can be classified as either *paramagnetic* or *diamagnetic* according to their behavior in a magnetic field. A paramagnetic substance is attracted into a magnetic field with a force that is proportional to the product of the field strength and field gradient. A diamagnetic substance, on the other hand, is repelled by a magnetic field.

In general, atoms and molecules with unpaired electrons $(S \neq 0)$ are paramagnetic. Since electrons possess spin, an unpaired electron creates a *permanent magnetic moment*. There is in many cases a further contribution to the permanent magnetic moment as a result of the movement of the electron in its orbital about the nucleus (or nuclei, in the case of molecules). In addition to the permanent paramagnetic moment, magnetic moments are *induced* in atoms and molecules on the application of an external magnetic field. Such induced moments are opposite to the direction of the field; thus repulsion occurs. The magnitude of this repulsion is a measure of the diamagnetism of the atom or molecule in question.

The paramagnetism of atoms and small molecules that results from unpaired electrons is larger than the induced diamagnetism; thus these substances are attracted into a magnetic field. Atoms and molecules with no unpaired electrons $(S = 0)$, and therefore no paramagnetism due to *electron spin*, are diamagnetic and are repelled by a magnetic field.

The H_2^+ ion, with one unpaired electron $(S = \frac{1}{2})$, is *paramagnetic*.

The H_2 molecule, with its two electrons paired $(S = 0)$, is *diamagnetic*.

2-9 SECOND-ROW HOMONUCLEAR DIATOMIC MOLECULES

Let us proceed now to the atoms in the second row of the periodic table, namely, Li, Be, B, C, N, O, F, and Ne. These atoms have $2s$, $2p_x$, $2p_y$, and $2p_z$ valence orbitals. We first need to specify a coordinate system for the general homonuclear diatomic molecule A_2, since the $2p$ orbitals have directional properties. The z axis is customarily assigned to be the *unique molecular axis*, as shown in Fig. 2–10. The molecular orbitals are obtained by adding and subtracting those atomic orbitals that overlap.

σ Orbitals

The $2s$ and $2p_z$ orbitals combine to give σ molecular orbitals, as illustrated in Fig. 2–11. The normalized wave functions are:

$$\psi(\sigma_s^b) = \frac{1}{\sqrt{2}}(2s_a + 2s_b) \tag{2-26}$$

$$\psi(\sigma_s^*) = \frac{1}{\sqrt{2}}(2s_a - 2s_b) \tag{2-27}$$

$$\psi(\sigma_z^b) = \frac{1}{\sqrt{2}}(2p_{z_a} + 2p_{z_b}) \tag{2-28}$$

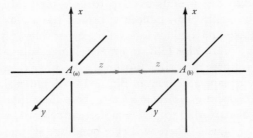

Figure 2–10   Coordinate system for an A_2 molecule.

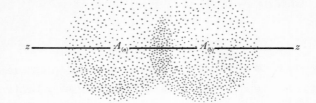

(a) overlap of 2s valence orbitals

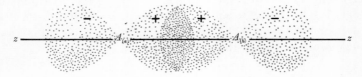

(b) overlap of $2p_z$ valence orbitals

**Figure 2–11   (a) Overlap of two 2s valence orbitals in A₂.
(b) Overlap of two $2p_z$ valence orbitals in A₂.**

$$\psi(\sigma_z^*) = \frac{1}{\sqrt{2}}(2p_{z_a} - 2p_{z_b}) \qquad (2\text{–}29)$$

Notice that the σ_z molecular orbitals are symmetric for rotation about the z axis.

π Orbitals

The $2p_x$ and $2p_y$ orbitals are not symmetric for rotation about the z axis.   The two $2p_x$ orbitals overlap to give the molecular orbital shown in Fig. 2–12.   This molecular orbital has a plus lobe on one side of the z axis and a minus lobe on the other side.   So if we rotate the molecular orbital by 180°, it simply changes sign.   Multiplication by -1 restores the original orbital.   In other words, there is a node in the yz plane as shown in Fig. 2–13.   A molecular orbital of this type is called a π *molecular orbital*.   It is clear that the two $2p_y$ orbitals can also overlap to give π molecular orbitals, which have a node in the xz plane.   There will be π bonding (π^b) and π antibonding (π^*) molecular orbitals; the more stable π^b orbitals will have a

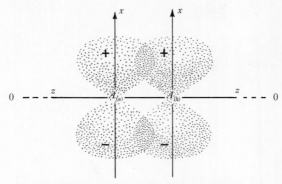

Figure 2–12   Overlap of two $2p_x$ orbitals in A$_2$.

concentration of electron density between the two A nuclei, whereas the less stable π^* orbital will have a node between the two nuclei. Boundary surfaces of the σ and π molecular orbitals for A$_2$ molecules with $2s$ and $2p$ valence orbitals are shown in Fig. 2–14.   The normalized wave functions for the π MO's follow:

$$\psi(\pi_x{}^b) = \frac{1}{\sqrt{2}}(2p_{x_a} + 2p_{x_b}) \qquad (2\text{–}30)$$

$$\psi(\pi_x{}^*) = \frac{1}{\sqrt{2}}(2p_{x_a} - 2p_{x_b}) \qquad (2\text{–}31)$$

$$\psi(\pi_y{}^b) = \frac{1}{\sqrt{2}}(2p_{y_a} + 2p_{y_b}) \qquad (2\text{–}32)$$

$$\psi(\pi_y{}^*) = \frac{1}{\sqrt{2}}(2p_{y_a} - 2p_{y_b}) \qquad (2\text{–}33)$$

The energy-level diagram for the molecular orbitals that accept the valence electrons can now be estimated.   We know that the $2s$ level is considerably more stable than $2p$ in the atoms.   The red line at 1.85 eV in the emission spectrum of lithium is due to an electron falling from the $2p$ to the more stable $2s$ orbital.   In fluorine, the $2s$–$2p$ energy difference is over 20 eV.   Thus we place $2p$ above $2s$ in the energy-level diagram.[1]   Then the σ^b, σ^*, π^b, and π^* orbitals are placed with the bonding levels more stable than the antibonding levels in

---

[1] See Appendix for neutral-atom orbital energies.

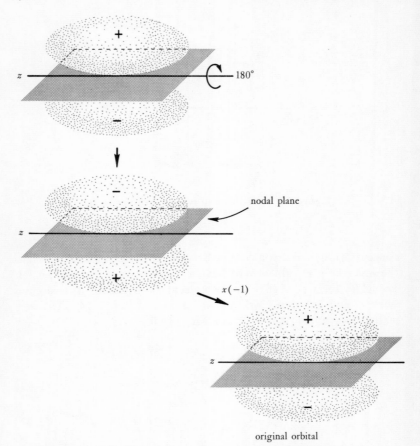

Figure 2–13   Rotation of a π molecular orbital by 180° about the internuclear axis.

any given combination.   The possible energy-level diagrams are shown in Fig. 2–15.

The relative positioning of the $\sigma_z{}^b$ level is uncertain.   When the $2s$–$2p$ energy difference is large, $\sigma_z{}^b$ is probably more stable than $\pi_{x,y}{}^b$, as shown in Fig. 2–15a.   We should emphasize here that it is a good approximation to consider the σ_s molecular orbitals as com-

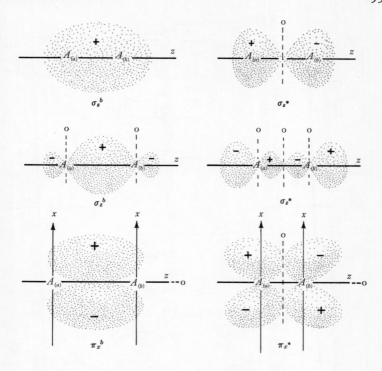

$\pi_y{}^b$ and $\pi_y{}^*$ are equivalent to $\pi_x{}^b$ and $\pi_x{}^*$

Figure 2–14 Boundary surfaces of the σ and π molecular orbitals formed from s and p valence orbitals for a homonuclear diatomic molecule.

posed of the two $2s$ atomic orbitals only if the $2s$–$2p$ energy difference is large. For small $2s$–$2p$ energy differences, we must consider the two $2s$ and the two $2p_z$ orbitals together in an LCAO–MO scheme. The most stable MO would be the combination

$$\psi(\sigma_s{}^b) = \frac{1}{\sqrt{2(1 + \tau^2)}}(2s_a + \tau 2p_{z_a} + 2s_b + \tau 2p_{z_b})$$

where the coefficient τ is less than unity and represents the amount of $2p$ included in the $\sigma_s{}^b$ MO.

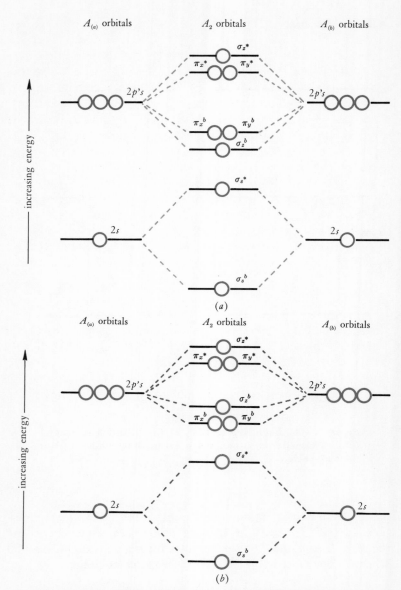

Figure 2–15 Molecular-orbital energy-level diagrams for a homonuclear diatomic molecule (*a*) with no σ_s–σ_z interaction; (*b*) with appreciable σ_s–σ_z interaction.

54

The stabilization of $\sigma_s{}^b$ and $\sigma_s{}^*$ resulting from such *s–p hybridiza-tion* is accompanied by a corresponding destabilization of $\sigma_z{}^b$ and $\sigma_z{}^*$, these latter orbitals acquiring some $2s$ character in the process. This effect is shown schematically in Fig. 2–16.

The final result for any reasonable amount of *s–p* mixing is that the $\sigma_z{}^b$ orbital becomes less stable than $\pi_{x,y}{}^b$, as shown in Fig. 2–15*b*. As we shall see in the pages to follow, *all diatomic molecules for which there is reliable experimental information have $\sigma_z{}^b$ more unstable than $\pi_{x,y}{}^b$.*

In Fig. 2–15 the $\pi_x{}^b$ and $\pi_y{}^b$ levels are shown on the same line. There is no difference in overlap in the π_x and π_y molecular orbitals and thus they have the same energy, or, in the jargon of the profes-sion, they are *degenerate*.

Using the molecular-orbital energy levels in Fig. 2–15, we shall discuss the electronic configurations of the second-row A_2 molecules.

Li_2

The lithium atom has one $2s$ valence electron. In Li, the $2s$–$2p$ energy difference is small and the $\sigma_s{}^b$ MO of Li_2 undoubtedly has considerable $2p$ character. The two valence electrons in Li_2 occupy the $\sigma_s{}^b$ MO, giving the ground-state configuration $(\sigma_s{}^b)^2$. Consistent with the theory, experimental measurements show that the lithium

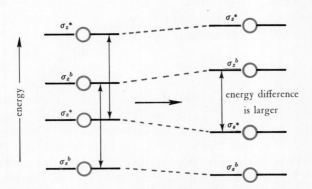

Figure 2–16   Schematic drawing of the effect of σ_s–σ_z interac-tion on the energies of $\sigma_s{}^b$, $\sigma_s{}^*$, $\sigma_z{}^b$, and $\sigma_z{}^*$.

molecule has no unpaired electrons. With two electrons in a bonding MO, there is one net bond. The bond length of Li_2 is 2.67 A as compared with 0.74 A for H_2. The larger R for Li_2 is partially due to the shielding of the two $\sigma_s{}^b$ valence electrons by the electrons in the inner $1s$ orbitals. This shielding reduces the attractions of the nuclei and the electrons in the $\sigma_s{}^b$ MO. The mutual repulsion of the two $1s$ electron pairs, an interaction not present in H_2, is also partly responsible for the large R of Li_2. The bond energies of H_2 and Li_2 are 103 and 25 kcal/mole, respectively. The smaller bond energy of Li_2 is again undoubtedly due to the presence of the two $1s$ electron pairs, as discussed above.

Be_2

The beryllium atom has the valence electronic structure $2s^2$. The electronic configuration of Be_2 would be $(\sigma_s{}^b)^2(\sigma_s{}^*)^2$. This configuration gives no net bonds $[(2-2)/2 = 0]$ and thus is consistent with the absence of Be_2 from the family of A_2 molecules.

B_2

Boron is $2s^22p^1$. The electronic configuration of B_2 depends on the relative positioning of the $\sigma_z{}^b$ and the $\pi_{x,y}{}^b$ levels. Experimental measurements indicate that the boron molecule has *two unpaired electrons* in the $\pi_{x,y}{}^b$ level. Thus the electronic configuration of B_2 is $(\sigma_s{}^b)^2(\sigma_s{}^*)^2(\pi_x{}^b)(\pi_y{}^b)$, giving one net π bond. The bond length of B_2 is 1.59 A. The bond energy of B_2 is 69 kcal/mole.

C_2

Carbon is $2s^22p^2$. In carbon the $\sigma_z{}^b$ and $\pi_{x,y}{}^b$ levels are so spaced that both the $(\sigma_s{}^b)^2(\sigma_s{}^*)^2(\pi_{x,y}{}^b)^4$ and the $(\sigma_s{}^b)^2(\sigma_s{}^*)^2(\pi_{x,y}{}^b)^3(\sigma_z{}^b)$ configurations have approximately the same energy. The latest view is that the configuration $(\sigma_s{}^b)^2(\sigma_s{}^*)^2(\pi_{x,y}{}^b)^4$ is the ground state (by less than 0.1 eV). In this state there are no unpaired electrons and a total of two π bonds. The two bonds predicted for C_2 may be compared with the experimentally observed bond energy of 150 kcal/mole and the bond length of 1.31 A.

N_2

Nitrogen is $2s^2 2p^3$. The electronic configuration of N_2 is $(\sigma_s{}^b)^2$ $(\sigma_s{}^*)^2(\pi_{x,y}{}^b)^4(\sigma_z{}^b)^2$, consistent with the observed diamagnetism of this molecule. The nitrogen molecule has three net bonds (one σ and two π), the maximum for an A_2 molecule, thus accounting for its unusual stability, its extraordinarily large bond energy of 225 kcal/mole, and its very short R of 1.10 A.

We wish to emphasize here that the highest filled orbital in N_2 is $\sigma_z{}^b$, which is contrary to the popular belief that $\pi_{x,y}{}^b$ is the higher level. The proof is that, on ionization of one electron from N_2, giving $N_2{}^+$, a $\sigma_z{}^b$ electron is lost, giving the structure $(\sigma_s{}^b)^2(\sigma_s{}^*)^2(\pi_{x,z}{}^b)^4(\sigma_z{}^b)$.

O_2

Oxygen is $2s^2 2p^4$. The electronic configuration of O_2 is $(\sigma_s{}^b)^2$ $(\sigma_s{}^*)^2(\sigma_z{}^b)^2(\pi_{x,y}{}^b)^4(\pi_x{}^*)(\pi_y{}^*)$. The electrons in $\pi_{x,y}{}^*$ have the same spin in the ground state, resulting in a prediction of *two unpaired electrons* in O_2; the oxygen molecule is paramagnetic to the extent of two unpaired spins in agreement with theory. The explanation of the paramagnetism of O_2 gave added impetus to the use of the molecular-orbital theory, since from the simple Lewis picture it is not at all clear why O_2 should have two unpaired electrons.

Two net bonds (one σ, one π) are predicted for O_2. The bond energy of O_2 is 118 kcal/mole, and $R = 1.21$ A. The change in bond length on changing the number of electrons in the $\pi_{x,y}{}^*$ level of the O_2 system is very instructive. The accurate bond length of O_2 is 1.2074 A. When an electron is removed from $\pi_{x,y}{}^*$, giving $O_2{}^+$, the bond length *decreases* to 1.1227 A. Formally, the number of bonds has increased from 2 to $2\frac{1}{2}$. When an electron is added to the $\pi_{x,y}{}^*$ level of O_2, giving $O_2{}^-$, the bond length *increases* to 1.26 A; addition of a second electron to give $O_2{}^{2-}$ increases the bond length still further to 1.49 A. This is in agreement with the prediction of $1\frac{1}{2}$ bonds for $O_2{}^-$ and 1 bond for $O_2{}^{2-}$.

F_2

Fluorine is $2s^2 2p^5$. The electronic configuration of F_2 is $(\sigma_s{}^b)^2$ $(\sigma_s{}^*)^2(\sigma_z{}^b)^2(\pi_{x,y}{}^b)^4(\pi_{x,y}{}^*)^4$, leaving no unpaired electrons and one net bond. This electronic structure is consistent with the diamagnetism of F_2, the 36-kcal/mole F—F bond energy, and the R of 1.42 A.

Ne_2

Neon has a closed-shell electronic configuration $2s^2 2p^6$. The hypothetical Ne_2 would have the configuration $(\sigma_s{}^b)^2 (\sigma_s{}^*)^2 (\sigma_z{}^b)^2 (\pi_{x,y}{}^b)^4$ $(\pi_{x,y}{}^*)^4 (\sigma_z{}^*)^2$ and zero net bonds. To date there is no experimental evidence for the existence of a stable neon molecule.

2-10   OTHER A_2 MOLECULES

With proper adjustment of the n quantum number of the valence orbitals, the MO energy-level diagrams shown in Fig. 2–15 for second-row A_2 molecules can be used to describe the electronic structures of A_2 molecules in general.

Na_2, K_2, Rb_2, Cs_2

The alkali metal diatomic molecules all have the ground-state configuration $(\sigma_s{}^b)^2$, with one σ bond. They are diamagnetic. The bond lengths and bond energies of Li_2, Na_2, K_2, Rb_2, and Cs_2 are given in Table 2–1. The bond lengths increase and the bond energies de-

Table 2-1

Bond Lengths and Bond Energies of Alkali Metal Molecules[a]

Molecule	Bond length, A	Bond energy, kcal/mole
Li_2	2.672	25
Na_2	3.078	17.3
K_2	3.923	11.8
Rb_2		10.8
Cs_2		10.4

[a]Data from T. L. Cottrell, *The Strengths of Chemical Bonds*, Butterworths, London, 1958, Table 11.5.1.

crease, regularly, from Li_2 to Cs_2. These effects presumably are due to the increased shielding of the $\sigma_s{}^b$ electrons by inner-shell electrons in going from Li_2 to Cs_2.

Cl_2, Br_2, I_2

The ground-state electronic configuration of the halogen molecules is $(\sigma_s{}^b)^2(\sigma_s{}^*)^2(\sigma_z{}^b)^2(\pi_{x,y}{}^b)^4(\pi_{x,y}{}^*)^4$, indicating one net σ bond. The molecules are diamagnetic. Table 2–2 gives bond lengths and bond energies for F_2, Cl_2, Br_2, and I_2. The bond lengths increase predictably from F_2 to I_2, but the bond energies are irregular, increasing from F_2 to Cl_2 and then decreasing from Cl_2 to I_2. The fact that the bond energy of Cl_2 is larger than that of F_2 is believed to be due to the smaller repulsions of electron pairs in the π orbitals of Cl_2. One explanation which has been advanced is that the reduced repulsions follow from the interaction of the empty chlorine $3d$ orbitals in the π MO system. As a result of such p_π–d_π interaction, the electron pairs in Cl_2 have a greater chance to avoid each other. However, it is not necessary to use the p_π–d_π explanation, since we know from atomic spectra that the interelectronic repulsions in the $2p$ orbitals of F are considerably larger than the repulsions in the $3p$ orbitals of Cl.

Table 2-2
Bond Lengths and Bond Energies of Halogen Molecules[a]

Molecule	Bond length, A	Bond energy, kcal/mole
F_2	1.418	36
Cl_2	1.988	57.07
Br_2	2.283	45.46
I_2	2.667	35.55

[a]Data from T. L. Cottrell, *The Strengths of Chemical Bonds*, Butterworths, London, 1958, Table 11.5.1.

Table 2-3

Quantum Number Assignments for Molecular Orbitals in Linear Molecules

Molecular orbitals	m_l	Atomic orbitals
σ	0	s, p_z, d_{z^2}
π	± 1	p_x, p_y, d_{xz}, d_{yz}
δ	± 2	$d_{xy}, d_{x^2-y^2}$

2-11 TERM SYMBOLS FOR LINEAR MOLECULES

Electronic states of a linear molecule may be classified conveniently in terms of angular momentum and spin, analogous to the Russell-Saunders term-symbol scheme for atoms. The unique molecular axis in linear molecules is labeled the z axis. The *combining atomic orbitals* in any given molecular orbital have the same m_l value. Thus an m_l quantum number is assigned to each different type of MO, as indicated in Table 2–3. The term designations are of the form

$$^{2S+1}|M_L|$$

where S has the same significance as for atoms. The M_L-state abbreviations are given in Table 2–4.

We shall work two examples in order to illustrate the procedure.

Table 2-4

State Symbols Corresponding to M_L Values in Linear-Molecule Electronic-State Classification

State	M_L
Σ	0
Π	± 1
Δ	± 2
Φ	± 3

EXAMPLE 2-1

The ground-state term of H_2 is found as follows.

1. Find M_L: The two electrons are placed in the σ^b MO shown in Fig. 2-8, giving the $(\sigma^b)^2$ configuration. This is the most stable state of H_2. The MO is σ type, so each electron has $m_l = 0$. Then

$$M_L = m_{l_1} + m_{l_2} = 0 + 0 = 0$$

and the state is Σ.

2. Find M_S: Since both electrons have $m_l = 0$, they must have different m_s values (the Pauli principle). Thus,

$$M_S = m_{s_1} + m_{s_2} = (+\tfrac{1}{2}) + (-\tfrac{1}{2}) = 0$$

with $M_S = 0$, $S = 0$. The correct term symbol[1] is therefore $^1\Sigma$.

From the result in the H_2 case, you may suspect that filled molecular orbitals always give $M_L = 0$ and $M_S = 0$. Indeed this is so, since in filled orbitals every positive m_l value is matched with a canceling negative m_l value. The same is true for the m_s values; they come in $+\tfrac{1}{2}$, $-\tfrac{1}{2}$ pairs in filled orbitals. This information eliminates considerable work in arriving at the term symbols for states of molecules in which there are many electrons, since most of the electrons are paired in different molecular orbitals.

EXAMPLE 2-2

Let us now find the ground-state term for O_2. The electronic configuration of O_2 is $(\sigma_s^b)^2(\sigma_s^*)^2(\sigma_z^b)^2(\pi_{x,y}^b)^4(\pi_{x,y}^*)^2$. All the orbitals are filled and give $M_L = 0$ up to $\pi_{x,y}^*$. The two electrons in π^* can be arranged as shown in Table 2-5.

There is a term with $M_L = +2, -2$, and $M_S = 0$ $(S = 0)$; the term designation is $^1\Delta$. There is a term with $M_L = 0$ and $M_S = +1, 0, -1(S = 1)$; the term designation is $^3\Sigma$. This leaves one microstate unaccounted for, with $M_L = 0$ and $M_S = 0(S = 0)$; thus there is a $^1\Sigma$ term.

The ground state must be either $^1\Delta$, $^3\Sigma$, or $^1\Sigma$. According to

[1] There are additional designations possible in certain linear molecules, depending on the symmetry properties of the molecular wave function. For example, the complete symbol for the ground state of H_2 is $^1\Sigma_g{}^+$. A discussion of the complete notation is given in C. J. Ballhausen and H. B. Gray, *Introductory Notes on Molecular Orbital Theory*, Benjamin, New York, 1965, Chap. 3.

Table 2-5

M_L, M_S Values for Example 2-2

M_L	M_S		
	1	0	-1
2		$(\overset{+}{\pi}_x \overset{-}{\pi}_x)$	
1			
0	$(\overset{+}{\pi}_x \overset{+}{\pi}_y)$	$(\overset{+}{\pi}_x \overset{-}{\pi}_y)$ $(\overset{-}{\pi}_x \overset{+}{\pi}_y)$	$(\overset{-}{\pi}_x \overset{-}{\pi}_y)$
-1			
-2		$(\overset{+}{\pi}_y \overset{-}{\pi}_y)$	

Hund's first rule the ground state has the highest spin multiplicity; the ground state is therefore $^3\Sigma$. As we discussed earlier, the $^3\Sigma$ ground state predicted by the molecular-orbital theory is consistent with the experimental results, since O_2 is paramagnetic to the extent of two unpaired electrons ($S = 1$). Spectroscopic evidence also confirms the $^3\Sigma$ ground state for O_2.

In Table 2–6 are listed the ground-state terms and other pertinent information for several homonuclear diatomic molecules.

2–12   HETERONUCLEAR DIATOMIC MOLECULES

Two different atoms are bonded together in a *heteronuclear diatomic molecule*. A simple example for a discussion of bonding is lithium hydride, LiH.

The valence orbitals of Li are $2s$, $2p_x$, $2p_y$, and $2p_z$. The valence orbital of H is $1s$. Fig. 2–17 shows the overlap of the hydrogen $1s$ orbital with the $2s$, $2p_x$, $2p_y$, and $2p_z$ lithium orbitals. The first step is to classify the valence orbitals as σ or π types. The $1s$ of H and the $2s$ and $2p_z$ of Li are σ valence orbitals. Thus, the lithium $2s$ and

$2p_z$ orbitals can be combined with the $1s$ orbital of hydrogen. The $2p_x$ and $2p_y$ orbitals of Li are π valence orbitals and do not interact with the σ type $1s$ orbital of H. The overlap of $2p_x$ (or $2p_y$) with $1s$ is zero, as shown in Fig. 2–17.)

We shall now discuss the σ-molecular-orbital system in some detail. Since the $2s$ level of Li is more stable than the $2p$ level, it is a good approximation to consider the σ^b molecular orbital as composed mainly of the hydrogen $1s$ and the lithium $2s$ orbitals.

It is also important to note that the $1s$ orbital of H is much more stable than the $2s$ orbital of Li. We know that in the free atoms this stability difference is large, since the first ionization potential of Li $(1s^2 2s \rightarrow 1s^2)$ is 5.4 eV and the ionization potential of H is 13.6 eV. As a consequence of the greater stability of the hydrogen $1s$ orbital, an electron in the σ^b molecular orbital spends most of its time in the vicinity of the H nucleus.

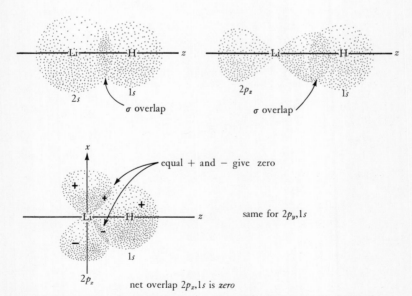

Figure 2–17 **Overlap of the hydrogen 1s orbital with the lithium valence orbitals.**

Table 2-6

Properties of Homonuclear Diatomic Molecules[a]

Molecule	Ground state	Bond length, A	Bond-dissociation energy, kcal/mole
Ag_2	$^1\sum$?		39
As_2	$^1\sum$		91
Au_2	$^1\sum$?		52
B_2	$^3\sum$	1.589	69
Bi_2	$^1\sum$		39.2
Br_2	$^1\sum$	2.283	45.46
C_2	$^1\sum(^3\Pi)$[b]	1.3117	150
Cd_2	$^1\sum$?		2.1
Cl_2	$^1\sum$	1.988	57.07
Cl_2^+	$^2\Pi$	1.891	
Cs_2	$^1\sum$		10.4
Cu_2	$^1\sum$		47
D_2	$^1\sum$	0.7416	
F_2	$^1\sum$	1.418	36
Ga_2			35
Ge_2			65
H_2	$^1\sum$	0.7415	103.24
H_2^+	$^2\sum$	1.06	61.06
He_2^+	$^2\sum$	1.08	
Hg_2	$^1\sum$		3.2
I_2	$^1\sum$	2.6666	35.55
K_2	$^1\sum$	3.923	11.8
Li_2	$^1\sum$	2.672	25
N_2	$^1\sum$	1.0976	225.0

(continued)

Table 2-6 *(continued)*

Molecule	Ground state	Bond length, A	Bond-dissociation energy, kcal/mole
N_2^+	$^2\Sigma$	1.116	
Na_2	$^1\Sigma$	3.078	17.3
O_2	$^3\Sigma$	1.20741	117.96
O_2^+	$^2\Pi$	1.1227	
O_2^-	$^2\Pi$?	1.26	
O_2^{2-}	$^1\Sigma$?	1.49	
P_2	$^1\Sigma$	1.8943	116.0
Pb_2			23
Rb_2	$^1\Sigma$		10.8
S_2	$^3\Sigma$	1.887	83
Sb_2	$^1\Sigma$		69
Se_2	$^1\Sigma$	2.152	65
Si_2		2.252	75
Sn_2			46
Te_2		2.59	53
Zn_2	$^1\Sigma$?		6

[a] Data from G. Herzberg, *Spectra of Diatomic Molecules*, Van Nostrand, New York, 1950, Table 39; T. L. Cottrell, *The Strengths of Chemical Bonds*, Butterworths, London, 1958, Table 11.5.1; L. E. Sutton (ed.), "Interatomic Distances," *Special Publication No. 11*, The Chemical Society, London, 1958.

[b] A short discussion of the ground state of C_2 can be found in J. W. Linnett, *Wave Mechanics and Valency*, Methuen, London, 1960, p. 134.

The σ^b orbital is shown in Fig. 2–18. The analytical expression for the σ^b MO of LiH has the form

$$\psi(\sigma^b) = C_1 2s + C_2 2p_z + C_3 1s \qquad (2\text{--}34)$$

In this case, $C_3 > C_1 > C_2$ and their numerical values are restricted by the normalization condition [Eq. (2–3)].

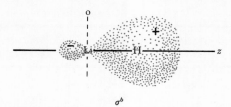

σ^b

Figure 2-18 Boundary surface of the σ bonding molecular orbital of LiH.

Since both the $2s$ and the $2p_z$ lithium orbitals are used in the σ molecular orbitals, there are two σ^* orbitals, one involving the $2s$ and one involving the $2p_z$. These σ^* orbitals are mainly localized on the Li, as shown in Fig. 2-19. The approximate wave functions are:

$$\psi(\sigma_s{}^*) = C_4 2s - C_5 1s; \qquad C_4 > C_5 \qquad\qquad (2\text{--}35)$$

$$\psi(\sigma_z{}^*) = C_6 2p_z - C_7 1s; \qquad C_6 > C_7 \qquad\qquad (2\text{--}36)$$

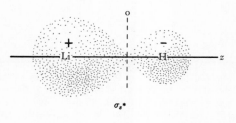

$\sigma_s{}^*$

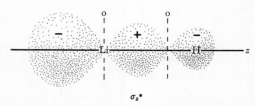

$\sigma_z{}^*$

Figure 2-19 Boundary surfaces of the $\sigma_s{}^*$ and $\sigma_z{}^*$ MO's of LiH.

2–13 MOLECULAR-ORBITAL ENERGY-LEVEL SCHEME FOR LiH

Figure 2–20 shows the MO energy-level scheme for LiH. The valence orbitals of Li are placed on the left side of the diagram, with the $2p$ level above the $2s$ level. On the right side, the hydrogen $1s$ level is shown. The $1s$ level of H is placed below the $2s$ level of Li, to agree with their known stability difference.

The σ^b and σ^* MO's are placed in the center. The σ^b MO is more stable than the hydrogen $1s$ valence orbital, and the diagram clearly shows that σ^b is mainly composed of hydrogen $1s$, with smaller fractions of lithium $2s$ and $2p_z$. The σ_s^* MO is less stable than the lithium $2s$ valence orbital, and the diagram shows that σ_s^* is composed of lithium $2s$ and hydrogen $1s$, with a much greater fraction of lith-

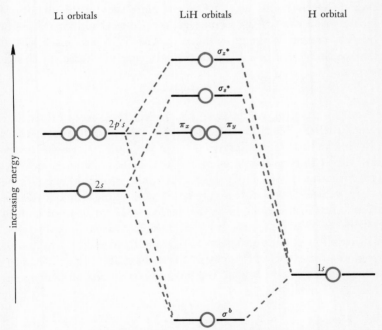

Figure 2–20 Relative orbital energies in LiH.

ium $2s$. The $\sigma_z{}^*$ orbital is shown less stable than $2p_z$, and it clearly has considerable $2p_z$ character.

The $2p_x$ and $2p_y$ orbitals of Li are shown in the MO column as π-type MO's. They are virtually unchanged in energy from the Li valence-orbital column, since H has no valence orbitals capable of π-type interaction.

2–14   GROUND STATE OF LiH

There are two electrons to place in the MO energy-level scheme for LiH shown in Fig. 2–20. This total is arrived at by adding together the one valence electron contributed by hydrogen ($1s$) and the one valence electron contributed by lithium ($2s$). Both electrons are accommodated in the σ^b MO, giving a ground-state configuration

$$(\sigma^b)^2 = {}^1\Sigma$$

Since the electrons in the σ^b MO spend more time in the vicinity of the H nucleus than of the Li nucleus, it follows that a separation of charge is present in the ground state. That is, the Li has a partial positive charge and the H has a partial negative charge, as shown below:

$$\text{Li}^{\delta+}\text{H}^{\delta-}$$

A limiting situation would exist if both electrons spent all their time around the H. The LiH molecule in that case would be made up of a Li^+ ion and a H^- ion; that is, $\delta = 1$. A molecule that can be formulated successfully as composed of ions is described as an *ionic molecule*. This situation is encountered in a diatomic molecule only if the valence orbital of one atom is very much more stable than the valence orbital of the other atom. The LiH molecule is probably not such an extreme case, and thus we say that LiH has *partial ionic character*. A calculation of the coefficients C_1, C_2, and C_3 would be required to determine the extent of this partial ionic character. One such calculation (unfortunately beyond the level of our discussion here) gives a charge distribution

$$\text{Li}^{0.8+}\text{H}^{0.8-}$$

which means that LiH has 80 per cent ionic character.

2–15 DIPOLE MOMENTS

A heteronuclear diatomic molecule such as LiH possesses an *electric dipole moment* caused by charge separation in the ground state. This electric moment is equal to the product of the charge and the distance of separation,

$$\text{dipole moment} = \mu = eR \qquad (2\text{--}37)$$

Taking R in centimeters and e in electrostatic units, μ is obtained in electrostatic units (esu). Since the unit of electronic charge is 4.8×10^{-10} esu and bond distances are of the order of 10^{-8} cm (1 A), we see that dipole moments are of the order of 10^{-18} esu. It is convenient to express μ in Debye units (D), with 10^{-18} esu $= 1$ Debye. If, as a first approximation, we consider the charges centered at each nucleus, R in Eq. (2–37) is simply the equilibrium internuclear separation R in the molecule.

Since it is possible to measure dipole moments, we have an experimental method of estimating the partial ionic character of heteronuclear diatomic molecules. The dipole moment of LiH is 5.9 Debye units (5.9 D). For $R = 1.60$ A (or 1.60×10^{-8} cm), we calculate for an ionic structure Li^+H^- a dipole moment of 7.7 D. Thus the partial charge from the dipole moment datum is estimated to be $5.9/7.7 = 0.77$, representing a partial ionic character of 77 per cent. This agrees with the theoretical value of 80 per cent given in the last section.

Dipole moments for a number of diatomic molecules are given in Table 2–7.

2–16 ELECTRONEGATIVITY

A particular valence orbital on one atom in a molecule which is more stable than a particular valence orbital on the other atom in a molecule is said to be more *electronegative*. A useful treatment of electronegativity was introduced by the American chemist Linus Pauling in the early 1930s. Electronegativity may be broadly defined as the ability of an atom in a molecule to attract electrons to itself. It must be realized, however, that each different atomic orbital in a molecule has a different electronegativity, and therefore atomic electronega-

Table 2-7
Dipole Moments of Some Diatomic Molecules[a]

Molecule	Dipole moment, D
LiH	5.88
HF	1.82
HCl	1.07
HBr	0.79
HI	0.38
O_2	0
CO	0.12
NO	0.15
ICl	0.65
BrCl	0.57
FCl	0.88
FBr	1.29
KF	8.60
KI	9.24

[a]Data from A. L. McClellan, *Tables of Experimental Dipole Moments*, Freeman, San Francisco, 1963.

tivities vary from situation to situation, depending on the valence orbitals under consideration. Furthermore, the electronegativity of an atom in a molecule increases with increasing positive charge on the atom.

The Pauling electronegativity value for any given atom is obtained by comparing the bond-dissociation energies of certain molecules containing that atom, in the following way. The bond-dissociation energy (DE) of LiH is 58 kcal/mole. The DE's of Li_2 and H_2 are 25 and 103 kcal/mole, respectively. We know that the DE's of Li_2 and H_2 refer to the breaking of purely covalent bonds—that is, that the two electrons in the σ^b levels are equally shared between the two hydrogen and the two lithium atoms, respectively. If the two electrons in the σ^b MO of LiH were equally shared between Li and H, we might expect to be able to calculate the DE of LiH from the geometric mean; thus

$$DE_{LiH} \overset{?}{=} \sqrt{DE_{H_2} \times DE_{Li_2}} \qquad (2\text{-}38)$$

This geometric mean is only 51 kcal/mole, 7 kcal/mole less than the observed DE of LiH. It is a very general result that *the DE of a molecule AB is almost always greater than the geometric mean of the DE's of A_2 and B_2*. An example more striking than LiH is the system BF. The DE's of B_2, F_2, and BF are 69, 36, and 195 kcal/mole, respectively. The geometric mean gives

$$DE_{BF} \overset{?}{=} \sqrt{69 \times 36} = 50 \neq 195 \qquad (2\text{-}39)$$

This "extra" bond energy in an AB molecule is presumably due to the electrostatic attraction of A and B in partial ionic form,

$$A^{\delta+}B^{\delta-}$$

Pauling calls the extra DE possessed by a molecule with partial ionic character the *ionic resonance energy* or Δ. Thus we have the equation

$$\Delta = DE_{AB} - \sqrt{D_{A_2} \times D_{B_2}} \qquad (2\text{-}40)$$

The electronegativity difference between the two atoms A and B is then defined as

$$\chi_A - \chi_B = 0.208\sqrt{\Delta} \qquad (2\text{-}41)$$

where χ_A and χ_B are electronegativities of atoms A and B and the factor 0.208 converts from kcal/mole to electron-volt units. The square root of Δ is used because it gives a more nearly consistent set of electronegativity values for the atoms. Since only *differences* are obtained from the application of Eq. (2-41), *one* atomic electronegativity value must be arbitrarily agreed upon, and then all the others are easily obtained. On the Pauling scale, the most electronegative atom, fluorine, is assigned an electronegativity (or EN) of approximately 4. The most recent EN values, calculated using the Pauling idea, are given in Table 2-8.

Another method of obtaining EN values was suggested by R. S. Mulliken, an American physicist. Mulliken's suggestion is that atomic electronegativity is the arithmetic mean of the ionization potential and the electron affinity of an atom; i.e.,

$$EN = \frac{IP + EA}{2} \qquad (2\text{-}42)$$

Table 2-8

Atomic Electronegativities

I	II	III	II	II	II	II	II	II	II	I	II	III	IV	III	II	I
H 2.20																
Li 0.98	Be 1.57											B 2.04	C 2.55	N 3.04	O 3.44	F 3.98
Na 0.93	Mg 1.31											Al 1.61	Si 1.90	P 2.19	S 2.58	Cl 3.16
K 0.82	Ca 1.00	Sc 1.36	Ti 1.54	V 1.63	Cr 1.66	Mn 1.55	Fe 1.83	Co 1.88	Ni 1.91	Cu 1.90	Zn 1.65	Ga 1.81	Ge 2.01	As 2.18	Se 2.55	Br 2.96
Rb 0.82	Sr 0.95	Y 1.22	Zr 1.33		Mo 2.16			Rh 2.28	Pd 2.20	Ag 1.93	Cd 1.69	In 1.78	Sn 1.96	Sb 2.05		I 2.66
Cs 0.79	Ba 0.89	La 1.10			W 2.36			Ir 2.20	Pt 2.28	Au 2.54	Hg 2.00	Tl 2.04	Pb 2.33	Bi 2.02		
		Ce 1.12	Pr 1.13 (III)	Nd 1.14 (III)		Sm 1.17 (III)		Gd 1.20 (III)		Dy 1.22 (III)	Ho 1.23 (III)	Er 1.24	Tm 1.25 (III)		Lu 1.27 (III)	
					U 1.38 (III)	Np 1.36 (III)	Pu 1.28 (III)									

[a] From A. L. Allred, *J. Inorg. Nucl. Chem.*, **17**, 215 (1961); roman numerals give the oxidation state of the atom in the molecules which were used in the calculations.

Equation (2–42) averages the ability of an atom to hold its own valence electron and its ability to acquire an extra electron. Of course the EN values obtained from Eq. (2–42) differ numerically from the Pauling values, but if the Mulliken values are adjusted so that fluorine has an EN of about 4, there is generally good agreement between the two schemes.[1]

2–17   IONIC BONDING

The extreme case of unequal sharing of a pair of electrons in an MO is reached when one of the atoms has a very high electronegativity and the other has a very small ionization potential (thus a small EN). In this case the electron originally belonging to the atom with the small IP is effectively transferred to the atom with the high EN,

$$M\cdot + X\cdot \rightarrow M^+ \ :X^- \tag{2–43}$$

The bonding in molecules in which there is an almost complete electron transfer is described as *ionic*. An example of such an ionic diatomic molecule is lithium fluoride, LiF. To a good approximation, the bond in LiF is represented as Li^+F^-. The energy required to completely separate the ions in a diatomic ionic molecule (Fig. 2–21) is given by the following expression:

potential energy = electrostatic energy + van der Waals energy

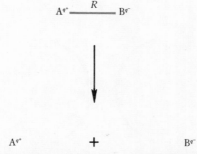

Figure 2–21   Dissociation of an ionic molecule into ions.

[1] However, note that the two scales are in different units.

The electrostatic energy is

$$\frac{q_1 q_2 e^2}{R} \tag{2-44}$$

where q_1 and q_2 are charges on atoms M and X and R is the internuclear separation.

There are two parts to the van der Waals energy. The most important at short range is the repulsion between electrons in the filled orbitals of the interacting atoms. This electron-pair repulsion is illustrated in Fig. 2–22. We have previously mentioned the mutual repulsion of filled inner orbitals, in comparing the bond energies of Li_2 and H_2.

The analytical expression commonly used to describe this interaction is

$$\text{van der Waals repulsion} = b e^{-aR} \tag{2-45}$$

where b and a are constants in a given situation. Notice that this repulsion term becomes very small at large R values.

The other part of the van der Waals energy is the attraction that results when electrons in the occupied orbitals on the different atoms correlate their movements in order to avoid each other as much as possible. For example, as shown in Fig. 2–23, electrons in orbitals on atoms M and X can correlate their movements so that an *instantaneous-dipole–induced-dipole attraction* results. This type of potential

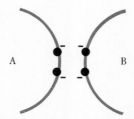

Figure 2–22 Repulsion of electrons in filled orbitals. This repulsion is very large when the filled orbitals overlap (recall the Pauli principle).

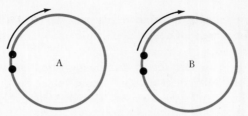

Figure 2–23 Schematic drawing of the *instantaneous-dipole–induced-dipole* interaction, which gives rise to a weak attraction.

energy is known as the *London dispersion energy*, and is defined by the expression

$$\text{London energy} = -\frac{d}{R^6} \qquad (2\text{–}46)$$

where d is a constant for any particular case. The reciprocal R^6 type of energy term falls off rapidly with increasing R, but not nearly so rapidly as the be^{-aR} repulsion term. Thus the London energy is more important than the repulsion at longer distances.

2–18 SIMPLE IONIC MODEL FOR THE ALKALI HALIDES

The total potential energy for an ionic alkali halide molecule is given by the expression

$$\text{PE} = \frac{-q_1 q_2 e^2}{R} + be^{-aR} - \frac{d}{R^6} \qquad (2\text{–}47)$$

We need only know the values of the constants b, a, and d in order to calculate potential energies from Eq. (2–47). The exact values of these constants for alkali metal ions and halide ions are not known. However, the alkali metal ions and the halide ions have inert-gas electronic configurations. For example, if LiF is formulated as an ionic molecule, Li^+ is isoelectronic with the inert gas He, and F^- is isoelectronic with the inert gas Ne. Thus the van der Waals interaction in Li^+F^- may be considered approximately equal to the van der Waals interaction in the inert-gas pair He–Ne. This inert-gas-pair approximation is of course applicable to the other alkali halide molecules as well.

The inert-gas-pair interactions can be measured and values for the b, a, and d constants are available. These values are given in Table 2–9. Using Eq. (2–47), we are now able to calculate the bond energy of LiF.

EXAMPLE

To calculate the bond energy of LiF, we first calculate the energy needed for the process

$$LiF \rightarrow Li^+ + F^-$$

We shall calculate this energy in atomic units (au). The atomic unit of distance is the Bohr radius, a_0, or 0.529 A. The atomic unit of charge is the electronic charge. The b, a, and d constants in

Table 2-9
van der Waals Energy Parameters[a]

Interaction pair	a	b	d
He—He	2.10	6.55	2.39
He—Ne	2.27	33	4.65
He—Ar	2.01	47.9	15.5
He—Kr	1.85	26.1	21.85
He—Xe	1.83	42.4	33.95
Ne—Ne	2.44	167.1	9.09
Ne—Ar	2.18	242	30.6
Ne—Kr	2.02	132	42.5
Ne—Xe	2.00	214	66.1
Ar—Ar	1.92	350	103.0
Ar—Kr	1.76	191	143.7
Ar—Xe	1.74	310	222.1
Kr—Kr	1.61	104	200
Kr—Xe	1.58	169	310
Xe—Xe	1.55	274	480

[a]All values are in atomic units. Data from E. A. Mason, *J. Chem. Phys.*, **23**, 49 (1955).

Table 2–9 are given in atomic units. Finally, 1 au of energy is equal to 27.21 eV. The bond length of LiF is 1.52 A; this is equal to $1.52/0.529 = 2.88$ au. For Li^+F^-, $q_1 = q_2 = 1$ au and $e^2 = 1$ au. Thus, on substitution of the b, a, and d parameters for He–Ne, Eq. (2–47) becomes

$$PE = \frac{-1}{2.88} + 33e^{(-2.27)(2.88)} - \frac{4.65}{(2.88)^6}$$

or

$$PE = -0.347 + 33(0.00144) - \frac{4.65}{571}$$

or

$$PE = -0.308 \text{ au} = -8.38 \text{ eV}$$

Accordingly, the energy required to separate Li^+ from F^- at a bond distance of 2.88 au is 8.38 eV. This is called the *coordinate-bond energy*. However, we want to calculate the standard *bond-dissociation energy*, which refers to the process

$$LiF \xrightarrow{\text{DE}} Li + F$$

That is, we need to take an electron from F^- and transfer it to Li^+:

$$LiF \xrightarrow{8.38 \text{ eV}} Li^+ + F^- \xrightarrow[+EA_F]{-IP_1(Li)} Li + F$$

We see that the equation which allows us to calculate the DE of an alkali halide is

$$DE = -PE - IP_1 + EA$$

Since $IP_1(Li) = 5.39$ eV and $EA_F = 3.45$ eV, we have finally

$$DE_{LiF} = 8.38 - 5.39 + 3.45 = 6.44 \text{ eV}$$

The calculated 6.45 eV, or 149 kcal/mole, compares favorably with the experimental DE of 137 kcal/mole.

Experimental bond energies and bond distances for the alkali halide molecules are given in Table 2–10. The alkali halides provide the best examples of ionic bonding, since, of all the atoms, the alkali metals have the smallest IP's; of course the halogens help by having very high EN's. The most complete electron transfer would be expected

Table 2-10
Bond Properties of the Alkali Halides[a]

Molecule	Bond length, A	Bond-dissociation energy, kcal/mole
CsF	2.345	121
CsCl	2.906	101
CsBr	3.072	91
CsI	3.315	75
KF	2.139[b]	118
KCl	2.667	101
KBr	2.821	91
KI	3.048	77
LiF	1.520[b]	137
LiCl	2.029[b]	115
LiBr	2.170	101
LiI	2.392	81
NaF	1.846[b]	107
NaCl	2.361	98
NaBr	2.502	88
NaI	2.712	71
RbF	2.242[b]	119
RbCl	2.787	102
RbBr	2.945	90
RbI	3.177	77

[a]Ground-state terms are $^1\Sigma$. Data from T. L. Cottrell, *The Strengths of Chemical Bonds*, Butterworths, London, 1958, Table 11.5.1

[b]Estimated values; see L. Pauling, *The Nature of the Chemical Bond*, Cornell Univ. Press, Ithaca, N.Y., 1960, p. 532.

in CsF and the least complete in LiI. In LiI, covalent bonding may be of considerable importance.

2-19   GENERAL AB MOLECULES

We shall now describe the bonding in a general diatomic molecule, AB, in which B has a higher electronegativity than A, and both A and B have *s* and *p* valence orbitals. The molecular-orbital energy levels for AB are shown in Fig. 2–24. The *s* and *p* orbitals of B are placed lower than the *s* and *p* orbitals of A, in agreement with the electronegativity difference between A and B. The σ and π bonding and antibonding orbitals are formed for AB in the same manner as for A$_2$, but with the coefficients of the valence orbitals larger for B in the bonding orbitals and larger for A in the antibonding orbitals. This means that the electrons in the bonding orbitals spend more time near the more electronegative B. In the unstable antibonding orbitals, they spend more time near the less electronegative A. The

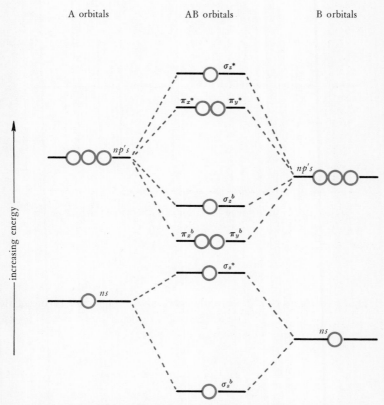

Figure 2–24   Relative orbital energies in a general AB molecule, with B more electronegative than A.

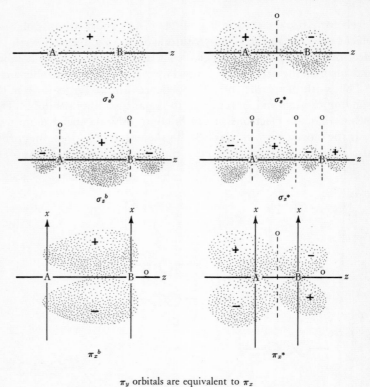

π_y orbitals are equivalent to π_x

Figure 2–25   Boundary surfaces of the MO's of an AB molecule, with B more electronegative than A.

boundary surfaces of the molecular orbitals for a general AB molecule are given in Fig. 2–25. The following specific cases illustrate the use of the bonding scheme shown in Fig. 2–24.

BN (8 Valence Electrons)

The ground-state electronic configuration for BN is $(\sigma_s{}^b)^2(\sigma_s{}^*)^2$ $(\pi_{x,y}{}^b)^3(\sigma_z{}^b)$. This gives a $^3\pi$ state and a prediction of two bonds

$(\frac{1}{2}\sigma, \frac{3}{2}\pi)$. The BN molecule is thus electronically similar to C_2. The bond lengths of C_2 and BN are 1.31 and 1.28 A, respectively. The BN bond energy is only 92 kcal/mole, as compared to 150 kcal/mole for C_2.

BO, CN, CO⁺ (9 Valence Electrons)

The BO, CN, and CO⁺ molecules all have the ground-state configuration $(\sigma_s{}^b)^2(\sigma_s{}^*)^2(\pi_{x,y}{}^b)^4(\sigma_z{}^b)$, and thus a $^2\Sigma$ ground state. There are $2\frac{1}{2}$ bonds predicted, which is $\frac{1}{2}$ more than for BN. The bond lengths are all shorter than that of BN (or C_2), being 1.20 A for BO, 1.17 A for CN, and 1.115 A for CO⁺. The bond energies are higher than that for BN, being 185 kcal/mole for BO and 188 kcal/mole for CN.

CO, NO⁺, CN⁻ (10 Valence Electrons)

The CO, NO⁺, and CN⁻ molecules are isoelectronic with N_2, having a $^1\Sigma$ ground state. The configuration $(\sigma_s{}^b)^2(\sigma_s{}^*)^2(\pi_{x,y}{}^b)^4(\sigma_z{}^b)^2$ predicts one σ and two π bonds. The bond lengths of NO⁺, CO, and CN⁻ increase with increasing negative charge, being 1.062 A for NO⁺, 1.128 A for CO, and 1.14 A for CN⁻. Comparing molecules having the same charge, the bond lengths of NO⁺, CO, and CN⁻ are shorter than those of BO, CN, and CO⁺, as expected. The bond energy of CO is 255.8 kcal/mole, which is even larger than the bond energy of 225 kcal/mole for N_2.

NO (11 Valence Electrons)

The electronic configuration of NO is $(\sigma_s{}^b)^2(\sigma_s{}^*)^2(\pi_{x,y}{}^b)^4(\sigma_z{}^b)^2$ $(\pi_{x,y}{}^*)$, giving a $^2\pi$ ground state. Since the eleventh electron goes into a π^* orbital, the number of bonds is now $2\frac{1}{2}$, or $\frac{1}{2}$ less than for NO⁺. The bond length of NO is 1.15 A, longer than either the CO or NO⁺ distances. The bond energy of NO is 162 kcal/mole, considerably less than the CO value.

The bond properties of a number of representative heteronuclear diatomic molecules are listed in Table 2–11.

Table 2-11
Properties of Heteronuclear Diatomic Molecules[a]

Molecule	Ground state	Bond length, A	Bond dissociation energy, kcal/mole
AlBr	$^1\textstyle\sum$	2.295	99
AlCl	$^1\textstyle\sum$	2.13	118
AlF	$^1\textstyle\sum$	1.65	158
AlH	$^1\textstyle\sum$	1.6482	67
AlI	$^1\textstyle\sum$		90
AlO	$^2\textstyle\sum$	1.6176	138
AsN	$^1\textstyle\sum$		115
AsO	$^2\Pi$		113
BBr	$^1\textstyle\sum$	1.88	97
BCl	$^1\textstyle\sum$	1.715	117
BF	$^1\textstyle\sum$	1.262	195
BH	$^1\textstyle\sum$	1.2325	70
BN	$^3\Pi$	1.281	92
BO	$^2\textstyle\sum$	1.2049	185
BaO	$^1\textstyle\sum$	1.940	130
BeCl	$^2\textstyle\sum$	1.7	69
BeF	$^2\textstyle\sum$	1.3614	92
BeH	$^2\textstyle\sum$	1.3431	53
BeO	$^1\textstyle\sum$	1.3308	124
BrCl	$^1\textstyle\sum$	2.138	52.1
BrF	$^1\textstyle\sum$	1.7555	55
BrH	$^1\textstyle\sum$	1.408	86.5
BrH+	$^2\Pi$	1.459	
CF	$^2\Pi$?	1.270	106

(continued)

Table 2-11 *(continued)*

Molecule	Ground state	Bond length, A	Bond dissociation energy, kcal/mole
CH	$^2\Pi$	1.1198	80
CN	$^2\sum$	1.1718	188
CN⁺		1.1727	
CN⁻		1.14	
CO	$^1\sum$	1.1282	255.8
CO⁺	$^2\sum$	1.1151	
CP	$^2\sum$	1.562	138
CS	$^1\sum$	1.5349	166
CSe	$^1\sum?$	1.66	115
CaO	$^1\sum$	1.822	100
ClF	$^1\sum$	1.6281	60.5
CsH	$^1\sum$	2.494	42
GaCl	$^1\sum$	2.208	115
GaF	$^1\sum$	1.775	142
GeO	$^1\sum$	1.650	157
HCl	$^1\sum$	1.2744	102.2
HCl⁺	$^2\Pi$	1.3153	
HD	$^1\sum$	0.7413	
HF	$^1\sum$	0.9175	134
HI	$^1\sum$	1.608	70.5
HS	$^2\Pi$	1.3503	80
IBr	$^1\sum$		41.90
ICl	$^1\sum$	2.32070	49.63
IF	$^1\sum$	1.985	46
InBr	$^1\sum$	2.5408	85

(continued)

Electrons and Chemical Bonding

Table 2-11 *(continued)*

Molecule	Ground state	Bond length, A	Bond dissociation energy, kcal/mole
InCl	$^1\sum$	2.4012	104
InF	$^1\sum$	1.9847	125
InH	$^1\sum$	1.8376	57
InI	$^1\sum$	2.86	65
KH	$^1\sum$	2.244	43
LiH	$^1\sum$	1.5953	58
MgO	$^1\sum$	1.749	92
NH	$^3\sum$	1.038	85
NH$^+$	$^2\Pi$	1.084	
NO	$^2\Pi$	1.150	162
NO$^+$	$^1\sum$	1.0619	
NP	$^1\sum$	1.4910	
NS	$^2\Pi$	1.495	115
NS$^+$		1.25	
NaH	$^1\sum$	1.8873	47
NaK	$^1\sum$		14.3
NaRb	$^1\sum$		13.1
OH	$^2\Pi$	0.9706	101.5
OH$^+$	$^3\sum$	1.0289	
PH	$^3\sum$	1.4328	
PN	$^1\sum$	1.4910	138
PO	$^2\Pi$	1.448	125
PbH	$^2\Pi$	1.839	42
PbO	$^1\sum$	1.922	94
PbS	$^1\sum$	2.3948	75

(continued)

Table 2-11 *(continued)*

Molecule	Ground state	Bond length, A	Bond dissociation energy, kcal/mole
RbH	$^1\Sigma$	2.367	39
SO	$^3\Sigma$	1.4933	119
SbO	$^2\Pi$		74
SiF	$^2\Pi$	1.603	88
SiH	$^2\Pi$	1.520	74
SiN	$^2\Sigma$	1.572	104
SiO	$^1\Sigma$	1.509	185
SiS	$^1\Sigma$	1.929	148
SnH	$^2\Pi$	1.785	74
SnO	$^1\Sigma$	1.838	132
SnS	$^1\Sigma$	2.06	110
SrO	$^1\Sigma$	1.920	83
TlBr	$^1\Sigma$	2.6181	78
TlCl	$^1\Sigma$	2.4848	87
TlF	$^1\Sigma$	2.0844	109
TlH	$^1\Sigma$	1.870	46
TlI	$^1\Sigma$	2.8136	65

[a]Data from G. Herzberg, *Spectra of Diatomic Molecules*, Van Nostrand, New York, 1950, Table 39; T. L. Cottrell, *The Strengths of Chemical Bonds*, Butterworths, London, 1958, Table 11.5.1; L. E. Sutton (ed.), "Interatomic Distances," *Special Publication No. 11*, The Chemical Society, London, 1958.

SUPPLEMENTARY PROBLEMS

1. Find the ground-state term for (a) B_2; (b) F_2; (c) C_2; (d) S_2.

2. Discuss the bond properties of N_2, P_2, As_2, Sb_2, and Bi_2 in terms of their electronic structures.

3. Discuss the bond properties of Cl_2 and Cl_2^+ using molecular-orbital theory.

4. Calculate the bond energies of (a) CsF; (b) CsBr; (c) NaI; (d) KCl. Compare your results with the experimental bond energies given in Table 2–10.

5. Work out the ground-state term for (a) BeF; (b) BeO. Calculate the bond energy of BeO, assuming ionic bonding.

6. Discuss the bond properties of the interhalogen diatomic molecules—ClF, BrCl, ICl, IBr, etc.

7. Discuss the bond properties of NO, PO, AsO, and SbO.

8. Formulate the bonding in the hydrogen halide molecules (HF, HCl, HBr, and HI) in terms of MO theory. Discuss the bond properties of these molecules.

III

Linear Triatomic Molecules

3–1 BeH₂

Let us investigate the molecular orbitals of BeH_2, a very simple linear triatomic molecule. As in a diatomic molecule, we tag the molecular axis the z axis (the H–Be–H line), as shown in Fig. 3–1. Beryllium has $2s$ and $2p$ valence orbitals; hydrogen has a $1s$ valence orbital. The molecular orbitals for BeH_2 are formed by using

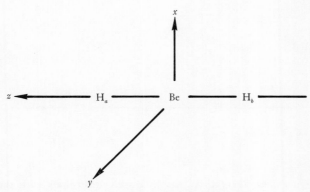

Figure 3–1 Coordinate system for BeH₂.

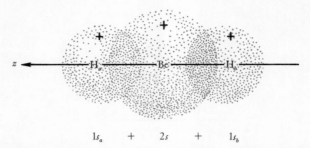

$$1s_a \quad + \quad 2s \quad + \quad 1s_b$$

Figure 3-2 Overlap of the hydrogen 1s orbitals with the beryllium 2s.

the $2s$ and $2p_z$ beryllium orbitals and the $1s$ orbitals of H_a and H_b. The proper linear combinations for the bonding molecular orbitals are obtained by writing the combinations of $1s_a$ and $1s_b$ that match the algebraic signs on the lobes of the central-atom (Be) $2s$ and $2p_z$ orbitals, respectively. This procedure gives a bonding orbital which *concentrates electronic density between the nuclei.* Since the $2s$ orbital does not change sign over the boundary surface, the combination $(1s_a + 1s_b)$ is appropriate (see Fig. 3-2). The $2p_z$ orbital has a plus lobe along $+z$ and a minus lobe along $-z$. Thus the proper combination of H orbitals is $(1s_a - 1s_b)$ (Fig. 3-3).

We have now described the two different σ^b molecular orbitals,

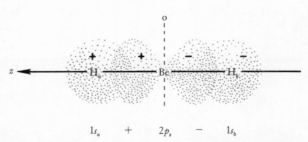

$$1s_a \quad + \quad 2p_z \quad - \quad 1s_b$$

Figure 3-3 Overlap of the hydrogen 1s orbitals with the beryllium $2p_z$.

which can be written as the following molecular-orbital wave functions:

$$\psi(\sigma_s{}^b) = C_1 2s + C_2(1s_a + 1s_b) \qquad (3\text{-}1)$$

$$\psi(\sigma_z{}^b) = C_3 2p_z + C_4(1s_a - 1s_b) \qquad (3\text{-}2)$$

The antibonding molecular orbitals corresponding to $\psi(\sigma_s{}^b)$ and $\psi(\sigma_z{}^b)$ will have nodes between the Be and the two H nuclei. That is, we shall combine the beryllium $2s$ with $-(1s_a + 1s_b)$ and the beryllium $2p_z$ with $-(1s_a - 1s_b)$. The two σ^* molecular orbitals are therefore

$$\psi(\sigma_s{}^*) = C_5 2s - C_6(1s_a + 1s_b) \qquad (3\text{-}3)$$

and

$$\psi(\sigma_z{}^*) = C_7 2p_z - C_8(1s_a - 1s_b) \qquad (3\text{-}4)$$

In order to describe these σ^b and σ^* orbitals in more detail, we must find good numerical values for the coefficients of the Be and H valence orbitals. Though there are reasonably good approximate methods for doing this, all are beyond the level of this book. However, since the beryllium $2s$ and $2p_z$ orbitals are much less stable than the hydrogen $1s$ orbitals (H is more electronegative than Be), we can confidently assume that the electrons in the bonding orbitals spend more time around the H nuclei—that is, that $2C_2{}^2 > C_1{}^2$ and $2C_4{}^2 > C_3{}^2$. In an antibonding orbital, an electron is forced to dwell mostly in the vicinity of the Be nucleus—that is, $C_5{}^2 > 2C_6{}^2$ and $C_7{}^2 > 2C_8{}^2$. (For further explanation of the relationships between the coefficients, see Problem 3-1.)

The $2p_x$ and $2p_y$ beryllium orbitals are not used in bonding, since they are π orbitals in a linear molecule and hydrogen has no π valence orbitals. These orbitals are therefore *nonbonding* in the BeH$_2$ molecule. The boundary surfaces of the BeH$_2$ molecular orbitals are given in Fig. 3-4.

3-2 ENERGY LEVELS FOR BeH$_2$

The molecular-orbital energy-level scheme for BeH$_2$, shown in Fig. 3-5, is constructed as follows: The valence orbitals of the central atom are indicated on the left-hand side of the diagram, with

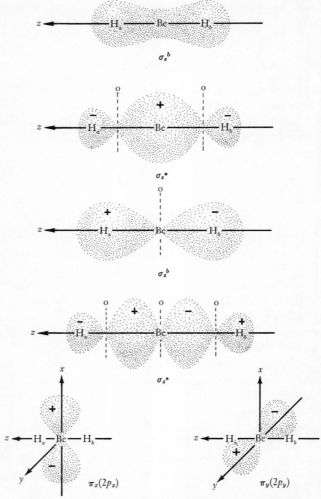

Figure 3-4   Boundary surfaces of the MO's of BeH₂.

Be orbitals BeH₂ orbitals H orbitals

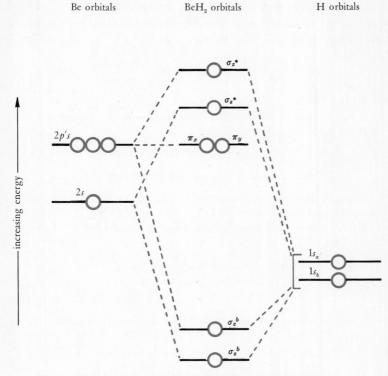

Figure 3–5 Relative orbital energies in BeH₂.

the more stable $2s$ level below the $2p$. The $1s$ orbitals of the two hydrogens are placed on the right-hand side of the diagram. The positioning of the $1s$ hydrogen orbitals lower than either $2s$ or $2p$ of beryllium is based on EN considerations. In the middle of the diagram are the molecular orbitals—bonding, nonbonding, and anti-bonding. As usual, bonding levels are more stable than their com-bining atomic orbitals, and antibonding levels are correspondingly less stable. The $2p_x$ and $2p_y$ nonbonding Be orbitals are not changed in energy in our approximation scheme. Thus they are simply moved out into the molecular-orbital column.

The ground state of BeH₂ is found by placing the valence electrons in the most stable molecular orbitals shown in Fig. 3–5. There are four valence electrons, two from beryllium $(2s)^2$ and two from the two hydrogen atoms. The ground-state electronic configuration is therefore

$$(\sigma_s{}^b)^2(\sigma_z{}^b)^2 = {}^1\Sigma$$

PROBLEM

3–1. Assume that the electronic charge density is distributed in the σ^b molecular orbitals as follows:

$$\sigma_s{}^b: \text{ Be, 30 per cent; 2H, 70 per cent}$$

$$\sigma_z{}^b: \text{ Be, 20 per cent; 2H, 80 per cent}$$

Calculate the wave functions for $\sigma_s{}^b$ and $\sigma_z{}^b$, as well as the final charge distribution in the BeH$_2$ molecule.

Solution. Since the normalization condition is $\int |\psi|^2 \, d\tau = 1$, we have for $\sigma_s{}^b$

$$\int |\psi(\sigma_s{}^b)|^2 \, d\tau = C_1{}^2 \int (2s)^2{}_{d\tau} + C_2{}^2 \int (1s_a)^2 \, d\tau + C_2{}^2 \int (1s_b)^2 \, d\tau$$
$$+ 2C_1C_2 \int (2s)(1s_a) \, d\tau + 2C_1C_2 \int (2s)(1s_b) \, d\tau$$
$$+ 2C_2{}^2 \int (1s_a)(1s_b) \, d\tau = 1$$

If the atomic orbitals $2s$, $1s_a$, and $1s_b$ are separately normalized, we have

$$\int |\psi(\sigma_s{}^b)|^2 \, d\tau = C_1{}^2 + C_2{}^2 + C_2{}^2 + \text{overlap terms} = 1$$

Making the simplifying assumption that the overlap terms are zero, we have finally

$$\int |\psi(\sigma_s{}^b)|^2 \, d\tau = C_1{}^2 + 2C_2{}^2 = 1$$

The probability for finding an electron in the $\sigma_s{}^b$ orbital if all space is examined is of course 1. The equation $C_1{}^2 + 2C_2{}^2 = 1$ shows that this total probability is divided, the term $C_1{}^2$ representing the probability for finding an electron in $\sigma_s{}^b$ around Be, and the term $2C_2{}^2$ the probability for finding an electron in $\sigma_s{}^b$ around the H atoms. Since the distribution of the electronic charge density is assumed to be 30 per cent for Be and 70 per cent for the H atoms in $\sigma_s{}^b$, the probabilities must be 0.30 for Be and 0.70 for the H atoms. Solving for the coefficients C_1 and C_2 in $\sigma_s{}^b$, we find

$$C_1{}^2 = 0.30 \quad \text{or} \quad C_1 = 0.548$$

and

$$2C_2{}^2 = 0.70 \quad \text{or} \quad C_2 = 0.592$$

Similarly, we have the equation $C_3{}^2 + 2C_4{}^2 = 1$ for $\sigma_z{}^b$; again solving for coefficients on the basis of our electronic-charge-density assumptions,

$$C_3{}^2 = 0.20 \quad\text{or}\quad C_3 = 0.447$$

and

$$2C_4{}^2 = 0.80 \quad\text{or}\quad C_4 = 0.632$$

The calculated wave functions are therefore

$$\psi(\sigma_s{}^b) = (0.548)2s + 0.592(1s_a + 1s_b)$$

and

$$\psi(\sigma_z{}^b) = (0.447)2p_z + 0.632(1s_a - 1s_b)$$

The ground-state configuration of BeH_2 is $(\sigma_s{}^b)^2(\sigma_z{}^b)^2$. The distribution of these four valence electrons over the Be and H atoms is calculated as follows:

Be $\sigma_s{}^b$: 2 electrons $\times\ C_1{}^2 = 2 \times 0.30 = 0.60$
   $\sigma_z{}^b$: 2 electrons $\times\ C_3{}^2 = 2 \times 0.20 = \underline{0.40}$
          total   1 electron

$H_a{=}H_b$ $\sigma_s{}^b$: 2 electrons $\times\ C_2{}^2 = 2 \times 0.35 = 0.70$
   $\sigma_z{}^b$: 2 electrons $\times\ C_4{}^2 = 2 \times 0.40 = \underline{0.80}$
        total   1.5 electrons

The BeH_2 molecule without the four valence electrons is represented

$$H^+\!-\!Be^{++}\!-\!H^+$$

Introducing the electrons as indicated above, we have the final charge distribution

$$\overset{-0.5}{H}\ \overset{+}{-Be-}\ \overset{-0.5}{H}$$

It is most important to note from these calculations that *the electronic charge densities associated with the nuclei in a normalized molecular orbital are given by the squares of the coefficients of the atomic orbitals (in the zero-overlap approximation).*

3–3   VALENCE-BOND THEORY FOR BeH_2

The molecular-orbital description of BeH_2 has the four electrons delocalized over all three atoms, in orbitals resembling the boundary-surface pictures shown in Fig. 3–4 ($\sigma_s{}^b$ and $\sigma_z{}^b$). We may, however, cling to our belief in the localized two-electron bond and consider that the four valence electrons in BeH_2 are in two equivalent bonding orbitals. By mixing together the $2s$ and $2p_z$ beryllium orbitals, we form two equivalent *sp hybrid orbitals*, as shown in Fig. 3–6. These two hybrid orbitals, sp_a and sp_b, overlap nicely with $1s_a$ and $1s_b$, respectively, and the bonding orbitals are (see Fig. 3–7):

$$\psi_1 = C_1 sp_a + C_2 1s_a \qquad (3\text{--}5)$$

$$\psi_2 = C_1 sp_b + C_2 1s_b \qquad (3\text{--}6)$$

The use of equivalent hybrid σ orbitals for the central atom is especially helpful for picturing the σ bonding in trigonal-planar and tetrahedral molecules.

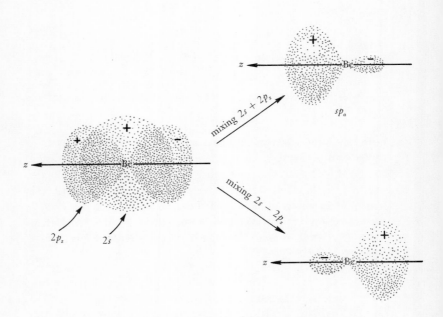

Figure 3–6   Formation of two sp hybrid orbitals.

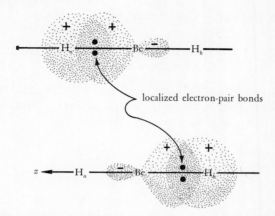

Figure 3–7   Valence bonds for BeH₂, using two equivalent *sp*
hybrid orbitals centered at the Be nucleus.

PROBLEM

3–2. Show that the general molecular-orbital description of BeH₂
is equivalent to the valence-bond description if, in Eqs. (3–1) and
(3–2), $C_1 = C_3$ and $C_2 = C_4$. (From the MO wave functions, construct the localized functions ψ_1 and ψ_2.)

3–4   LINEAR TRIATOMIC MOLECULES WITH π BONDING

The CO_2 molecule, in our standard coordinate system, is shown in
Fig. 3–8. This molecule is an example of a linear triatomic molecule
in which all three atoms have ns and np valence orbitals. The $2s$ and
$2p_z$ carbon orbitals are used for σ bonding, along with the $2p_z$ orbitals
on each oxygen.[1] The σ orbitals are the same as for BeH₂, except
that now the end oxygen atoms use mainly the $2p_z$ orbitals instead
of the $1s$ valence orbitals used by the hydrogen atoms. The σ wave
functions are:

$$\psi(\sigma_s{}^b) = C_1 2s + C_2(2p_{z_a} + 2p_{z_b}) \tag{3–7}$$

[1] The oxygen valence orbitals are $2s$ and $2p$. Thus a much better, approximate σ
MO scheme would include both $2s$ and $2p_z$ oxygen orbitals. For simplicity, however,
we shall only use the $2p_z$ oxygen orbitals in forming the σ MO's.

$$\psi(\sigma_s{}^*) = C_3 2s - C_4(2p_{z_a} + 2p_{z_b}) \tag{3-8}$$

$$\psi(\sigma_z{}^b) = C_5 2p_z + C_6(2p_{z_a} - 2p_{z_b}) \tag{3-9}$$

$$\psi(\sigma_z{}^*) = C_7 2p_z - C_8(2p_{z_a} - 2p_{z_b}) \tag{3-10}$$

The π molecular orbitals are made up of the $2p_x$ and $2p_y$ valence orbitals of the three atoms. Let us derive the π_x orbitals for CO_2. There are two different linear combinations of the oxygen $2p_x$ orbitals:

$$2p_{x_a} + 2p_{x_b} \tag{3-11}$$

$$2p_{x_a} - 2p_{x_b} \tag{3-12}$$

The combination $(2p_{x_a} + 2p_{x_b})$ overlaps the carbon $2p_x$ orbital as shown in Fig. 3–9. Since x and y are equivalent, we have the following π^b and π^* molecular orbitals:

$$\psi(\pi_x{}^b) = C_9 2p_x + C_{10}(2p_{x_a} + 2p_{x_b}) \tag{3-13}$$

$$\psi(\pi_y{}^b) = C_9 2p_y + C_{10}(2p_{y_a} + 2p_{y_b}) \tag{3-14}$$

$$\psi(\pi_x{}^*) = C_{11} 2p_x - C_{12}(2p_{x_a} + 2p_{x_b}) \tag{3-15}$$

$$\psi(\pi_y{}^*) = C_{11} 2p_y - C_{12}(2p_{y_a} + 2p_{y_b}) \tag{3-16}$$

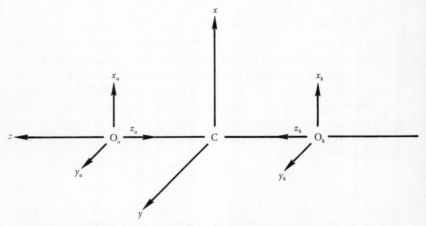

Figure 3–8   Coordinate system for CO_2.

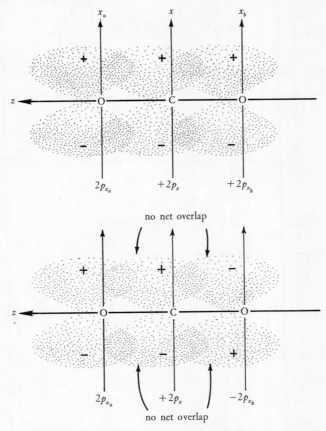

Figure 3–9   Overlap of the $2p_x$ orbitals of the carbon atom and the two oxygen atoms.

The combination $(2p_{x_a} - 2p_{x_b})$ has zero overlap with the carbon $2p_x$ orbital (see Fig. 3–9), and is therefore *nonbonding* in the molecular-orbital scheme.   We have, then, the normalized wave functions

$$\psi(\pi_x) = \frac{1}{\sqrt{2}}(2p_{x_a} - 2p_{x_b}) \tag{3-17}$$

and

$$\psi(\pi_y) = \frac{1}{\sqrt{2}}(2p_{y_a} - 2p_{y_b}) \tag{3-18}$$

The boundary surfaces of the MO's for CO_2 are shown in Fig. 3–10.
The MO energy-level scheme for CO_2 is given in Fig. 3–11. Notice

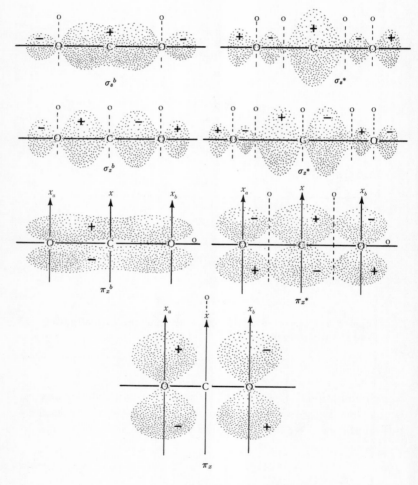

$\pi_y{}^b$, $\pi_y{}^*$, and π_y are equivalent to $\pi_x{}^b$, $\pi_x{}^*$, and π_x

Figure 3–10 Boundary surfaces of the MO's of CO_2.

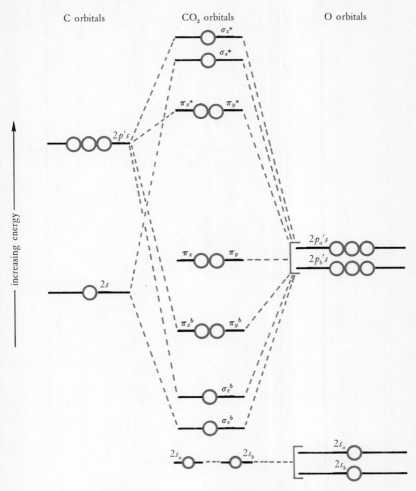

Figure 3–11   Relative orbital energies in CO_2.

that the oxygen orbitals are more stable than the carbon orbitals. There are 16 valence electrons (C is $2s^2 2p^2$; O is $2s^2 2p^4$) to place in the levels shown in the scheme. The ground state of CO_2 is therefore

$$(2s_a)^2 (2s_b)^2 (\sigma_s^b)^2 (\sigma_z^b)^2 (\pi_{x,y}^b)^4 (\pi_{x,y})^4 \qquad {}^1\Sigma$$

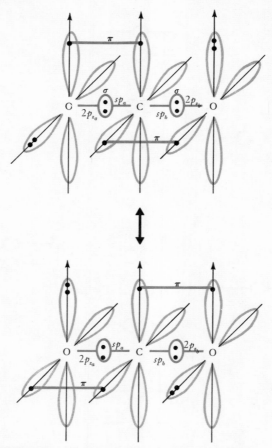

Figure 3–12   Valence-bond structures for CO₂.

There are four electrons in σ^b orbitals and four electrons in π^b orbitals. Thus we have two σ bonds and two π bonds for CO_2, in agreement with the two valence-bond structures shown in Fig. 3–12.

3–5   BOND PROPERTIES OF CO_2

The C—O bond distance in carbon dioxide is 1.162 A, longer than the C—O bond distance in carbon monoxide.   These bond lengths are consistent with the double bond ($C\!=\!O$) between C and O in CO_2 and the triple bond ($C\!\equiv\!O$) in CO.

There are two types of bond energies for CO_2. The bond-dissociation energy, which we discussed in Chapter II, refers to the breaking of a *specific* bond. In CO_2, the process

$$O\!-\!C\!-\!O \xrightarrow{\text{DE}} CO + O \qquad (3\text{-}19)$$

represents the dissociation of one oxygen from carbon dioxide, leaving carbon monoxide; this DE is 127 kcal/mole. However, the average C—O bond energy in CO_2 is obtained by completely splitting CO_2 into ground-state atoms, breaking both C—O bonds:

$$O\!-\!C\!-\!O \xrightarrow{E} C + O + O \qquad (3\text{-}20)$$

The average C—O bond energy (BE) is then one-half the value of E in Eq. (3–20). Obviously E is the sum of $DE(CO_2)$ and $DE(CO)$,

$$O\!-\!C\!-\!O \xrightarrow{\text{DE}(CO_2)} C\!-\!O + O \xrightarrow{\text{DE}(CO)} C + O + O \quad (3\text{-}21)$$

$$E = DE(CO_2) + DE(CO) = 127 + 256 = 383 \text{ kcal/mole}$$

and

$$\frac{E}{2} = BE(CO_2) \cong 192 \text{ kcal/mole} \qquad (3\text{-}22)$$

We shall use the abbreviations BE and DE in the bond-energy tables in this book.

The ground states, bond lengths, and bond energies for a number of linear triatomic molecules are given in Table 3–1.

3–6 IONIC TRIATOMIC MOLECULES: THE ALKALINE EARTH HALIDES

Molecules composed of atoms of the alkaline earth elements (Be, Mg, Ca, Sr, Ba) and halogen atoms are probably best described with the ionic model, since the electronegativity differences between alkaline earth and halogen atoms are large. Thus we picture the bonding as $X^-\!-\!M^{++}\!-\!X^-$. Let us illustrate bond-energy calculations for molecules of this type, using $CaCl_2$ as an example.

Table 3-1

Properties of Linear Triatomic Molecules[a]

Molecule	Ground state	Bond	Bond length, A	Bond energies, kcal/mole
$BeBr_2$	$^1\sum$	Br Be—Br Be—Br		89(BE)
$BeCl_2$	$^1\sum$	ClBe—Cl Be—Cl	1.74	147(DE) 109(BE)
BeI_2	$^1\sum$	IBe—I Be—I		69(BE)
CO_2	$^1\sum$	OC—O C—O	1.162	127(DE) 192(BE)
COS	$^1\sum$	OC—S	1.561	128(DE)
CS_2	$^1\sum$	SC—S C—S	1.554	128(BE)
CSe_2	$^1\sum$	C—Se		112(BE)
$CaCl_2$	$^1\sum$	ClCa—Cl Ca—Cl	2.54	176(DE) 113(BE)
$CdBr_2$	$^1\sum$	BrCd—Br	2.39	76(DE)
$CdCl_2$	$^1\sum$	ClCd—Cl	2.23	84(DE)
CdI_2	$^1\sum$	ICd—I	2.58	50(DE)
HCN	$^1\sum$	HC—N H—CN	1.153 1.066	207(DE) 114(DE)
$HgBr_2$	$^1\sum$	BrHg—Br Hg—Br	2.43	72(DE) 44(BE)
HgBrI	$^1\sum$	BrHg—I		64(DE)
$HgCl_2$	$^1\sum$	ClHg—Cl Hg—Cl	2.30	81(DE) 54(BE)
HgClBr	$^1\sum$	BrHg—Cl		77(DE)
HgClI	$^1\sum$	IHg—Cl ClHg—I		75(DE) 63(DE)

(continued)

Table 3-1 *(continued)*

Molecule	Ground state	Bond	Bond length, A	Bond energies, kcal/mole
HgF_2	$^1\Sigma$	FHg– F		100(DE)
		Hg– F		66(BE)
HgI_2	$^1\Sigma$	IHg– I	2.60	60(DE)
		Hg– I		35(BE)
NO_2^+	$^1\Sigma$	N–C	1.10	
$MgCl_2$	$^1\Sigma$	ClMg– Cl	2.18	136(DE)
		Mg– Cl		99(BE)
SiS_2	$^1\Sigma$	Si– S		70(BE)
$ZnCl_2$	$^1\Sigma$	ClZn– Cl	2.12	96(DE)
ZnI_2	$^1\Sigma$	IZn– I		53(DE)

[a]Data from T. L. Cottrell, *The Strengths of Chemical Bonds*, Butterworths, London, 1958, Table 11.5.1.

EXAMPLE

Our purpose is to calculate the average Ca—Cl bond energy in $CaCl_2$:

$$Cl_a^- \underline{\quad R \quad} Ca^{++} \underline{\quad R \quad} Cl_b^-$$

For $CaCl_2$ (or any MX_2) there are two attractions, Ca^{++}—Cl_a^- and Ca^{++}—Cl_b^-, each at a distance of R. In addition there is one repulsion, Cl_a^-—Cl_b^-, at a distance of $2R$. The sum of these electrostatic terms is represented

$$\text{electrostatic energy} = -\frac{2e^2}{R} - \frac{2e^2}{R} + \frac{e^2}{R} = -\frac{3.5e^2}{R}$$

The energy *per bond* is one-half $-3.5e^2/R$, or $-1.75e^2/R$. The van der Waals energy can be approximated again as an inert-gas-pair interaction. In this case we have one Ar–Ar interaction for each bond. The inert-gas-pair approximation of the van der Waals energy is not expected to be as good for the MX_2 molecules as for the

MX molecules, however, owing to the small size of M^{++} compared to that of the isoelectronic inert gas atoms (see Fig. 3–13). Thus the actual Ca^{++}—Cl^- van der Waals repulsion energy is probably less than that calculated.

The final expression for the energy of each Ca^{++}—Cl^- bond is

$$PE = \text{potential energy} = \frac{-1.75e^2}{R} + be^{-aR} - \frac{d}{R^6}$$

The Ca—Cl bond length in $CaCl_2$ is 2.54 A, or 4.82 au. On substituting the Ar–Ar parameters from Table 2–9, we have

$$PE = \frac{-1.75}{4.82} + 350e^{(-1.92)(4.82)} - \frac{103}{(4.82)^6}$$

or

$$PE = -0.337 \text{ au} = -9.17 \text{ eV}$$

The 9.17 eV is one-half the energy required to dissociate $CaCl_2$ into ions,

$$CaCl_2 \xrightarrow{E'} Ca^{++} + Cl^- + Cl^- \qquad E' = -2PE$$

For the average bond energy BE, we have the process

$$CaCl_2 \xrightarrow{E} Ca + Cl + Cl$$

$$E = E' + 2EA(Cl) - IP_1(Ca) - IP_2(Ca) \qquad \text{and} \qquad BE = \frac{E}{2}$$

With $EA(Cl) = 3.61$ eV, $IP_1(Ca) = 6.11$ eV, $IP_2(Ca) = 11.87$ eV, and $E' = 18.34$ eV, we obtain $E = 7.58$ eV or 175 kcal/mole and

Ar K^+ Ca^{2+}

Figure 3–13   Relative effective sizes of Ar, K^+, and Ca^{2+}.

BE(Ca—Cl) $\cong$ 88 kcal/mole. This calculated value of 88 kcal/mole may be compared with the experimental value of 113 kcal/mole. We see that the ionic model for $CaCl_2$ is not as good as the ionic model for the alkali halides. This is evidence that the alkaline earth halides have more "covalent character" than the alkali halides. Thus, it is likely that there are important covalent-bond contributions to the bond energy of $CaCl_2$.

Experimental bond energies for a number of alkaline earth halides are given in Table 3–1.

SUPPLEMENTARY PROBLEMS

1. Work out the ground-state term for the molecule N_3.

2. Calculate the Be—Cl bond energy in $BeCl_2$. The value of $IP_2(Be)$ is 18.21 eV.

3. Discuss the bonding in CO_2, CS_2, and CSe_2 in terms of MO theory. Compare the bond properties of these molecules.

IV

Trigonal-Planar Molecules

4–1 BF_3

$\mathbf{B}$oron trifluoride has a trigonal-planar structure, with all F—B—F *bond angles*[1] 120°. Boron has $2s$ and $2p$ orbitals that bond with the fluorine $2s$ and $2p$ orbitals. A convenient coordinate system for a discussion of bonding in BF_3 is shown in Fig. 4–1.

We need only one σ valence orbital from each fluorine. We shall use in the discussion only the $2p$ orbital, since the molecular orbitals derived are appropriate for any combination of $2s$ and $2p$. However, it is probable that the very stable fluorine $2s$ orbital is not appreciably involved in the σ bonding. The ionization potential of an electron in the $2s$ orbital of fluorine is over 40 eV.

4–2 σ MOLECULAR ORBITALS

The σ molecular orbitals are formed using the $2s$, $2p_x$, and $2p_y$ boron orbitals, along with the $2p_{z_a}$, $2p_{z_b}$, and $2p_{z_c}$ orbitals of the fluorine atoms. We must find the linear combinations of $2p_{z_a}$, $2p_{z_b}$, and $2p_{z_c}$ that give maximum overlap with $2s$, $2p_x$, and $2p_y$. The

---

[1] Bond angle is a commonly used term, meaning the angle between "internuclear lines."

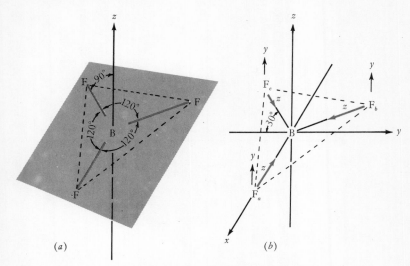

Figure 4–1   Coordinate system for BF₃.

boron $2s$ orbital is shown in Fig. 4–2.   The combination $(2p_{z_a} + 2p_{z_b} + 2p_{z_c})$ overlaps the $2s$ orbital.   Thus the molecular orbitals derived from the boron $2s$ orbital are (using the shorthand $z_a = 2p_{z_a}$, $z_b = 2p_{z_b}$, and $z_c = 2p_{z_c}$):

$$\psi(\sigma_s{}^b) = C_1 2s + C_2(z_a + z_b + z_c) \tag{4-1}$$

$$\psi(\sigma_s{}^*) = C_3 2s - C_4(z_a + z_b + z_c) \tag{4-2}$$

The boron $2p_y$ orbital is shown in Fig. 4–3.   The combination $(z_b - z_c)$ matches the positive and negative lobes of $2p_y$.   The molecular orbitals from $2p_y$ are:

$$\psi(\sigma_y{}^b) = C_5 2p_y + C_6(z_b - z_c) \tag{4-3}$$

$$\psi(\sigma_y{}^*) = C_7 2p_y - C_8(z_b - z_c) \tag{4-4}$$

The boron $2p_x$ orbital is shown in Fig. 4–4.   A combination $(z_a - z_b - z_c)$ correctly overlaps the lobes of $2p_x$.   There is a minor complication, however: the overlaps of z_a, z_b, and z_c with $2p_x$ are not the same.   Specifically, z_a points directly at the positive lobe of $2p_x$,

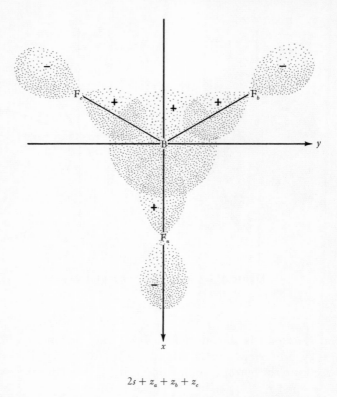

$$2s + z_a + z_b + z_c$$

Figure 4-2 **Overlap of the boron 2s orbital with the 2p_z orbitals of the fluorine atoms.**

whereas z_b and z_c are 60° displaced from a comparable overlap with the negative lobe. In order to relate z_a to z_b and z_c, we must find the fraction of $2p_x$ that can be resolved along the z_b line. This fraction is simply cos 60°, or $\frac{1}{2}$. We deduce that the *sum* $z_b + z_c$ gives the same overlap with $2p_x$ as z_a does alone. Then the proper combination is $(z_a - \frac{1}{2}z_b - \frac{1}{2}z_c)$, and the σ molecular orbitals from $2p_x$ are:

$$\psi(\sigma_x{}^b) = C_9 2p_x + C_{10}(z_a - \tfrac{1}{2}z_b - \tfrac{1}{2}z_c) \qquad (4\text{-}5)$$

$$\psi(\sigma_x{}^*) = C_{11} 2p_x - C_{12}(z_a - \tfrac{1}{2}z_b - \tfrac{1}{2}z_c) \qquad (4\text{-}6)$$

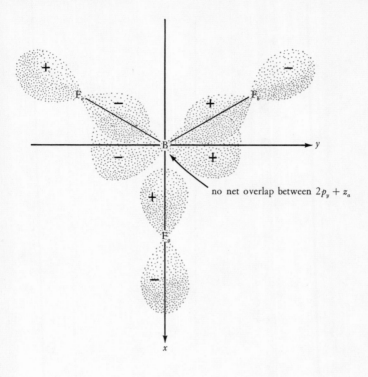

no net overlap between $2p_y + z_a$

$$2p_y + z_b - z_c$$

Figure 4–3 Overlap of the boron $2p_y$ orbital with the $2p_z$ orbitals of the fluorine atoms.

4–3 π MOLECULAR ORBITALS

The π molecular orbitals are formed using the boron $2p_z$ orbital and the $2p_y$ orbitals of the fluorine atoms.   The combination $(y_a + y_b + y_c)$ matches the $2p_z$ orbital, as shown in Fig. 4–5.   Thus the bonding and antibonding π molecular orbitals are:

$$\psi(\pi_z{}^b) = C_{13}2p_z + C_{14}(y_a + y_b + y_c) \qquad (4\text{–}7)$$

$$\psi(\pi_z{}^*) = C_{15}2p_z - C_{16}(y_a + y_b + y_c) \qquad (4\text{–}8)$$

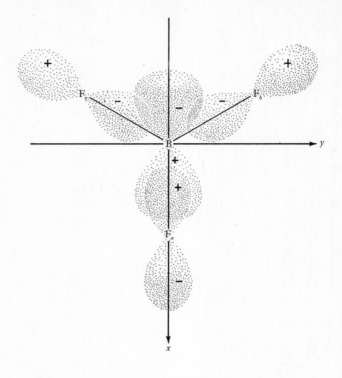

$$2p_x + z_a - z_b - z_c$$

Figure 4–4 Overlap of the boron $2p_x$ orbital with the $2p_z$ orbitals of the fluorine atoms.

Since we started with three fluorine $2p_y$ orbitals, there are two more independent linear combinations of y_a, y_b, and y_c. One satisfactory pair is $(y_a - y_c)$ and $(y_a - 2y_b + y_c)$. As shown in Fig. 4–6, these orbital combinations do not overlap the boron $2p_z$ orbital. Thus they are nonbonding in BF_3, and we have

$$\psi(\pi_1) = \frac{1}{\sqrt{2}}(y_a - y_c) \qquad (4\text{–}9)$$

$$\psi(\pi_2) = \frac{1}{\sqrt{6}}(y_a - 2y_b + y_c) \qquad (4\text{–}10)$$

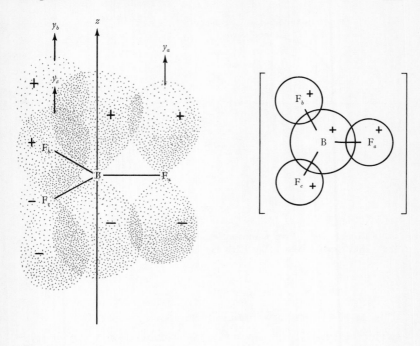

$2p_z + y_a + y_b + y_c$

Figure 4-5 Overlap of the boron $2p_z$ orbital with the $2p_y$ orbitals of the fluorine atoms.

4-4 ENERGY LEVELS FOR BF_3

The molecular-orbital energy-level scheme for BF_3 is shown in Fig. 4-7. The fluorine valence orbitals are more stable than the boron valence orbitals, and so electrons in bonding molecular orbitals spend more time in the domain of the fluorine nuclei. The σ_x and σ_y molecular orbitals are degenerate in trigonal-planar molecules such as BF_3. Since this is by no means obvious from Eqs. (4-3), (4-4), (4-5), and (4-6), we shall devote a short section to an explanation.

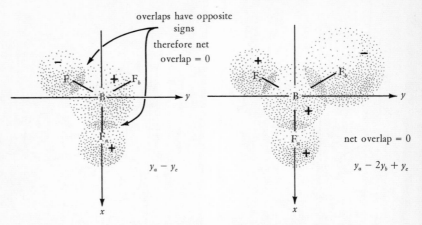

Figure 4–6 Two combinations of the fluorine $2p_y$ orbitals that have zero overlap with the boron $2p_z$ orbital.

4–5 EQUIVALENCE OF σ_x AND σ_y ORBITALS

The total overlap of the normalized combination $\sqrt{\frac{2}{3}}(z_a - \frac{1}{2}z_b - \frac{1}{2}z_c)$ with $2p_x$ will be called $S(\sigma_x)$; the total overlap of $(1/\sqrt{2})$ $(z_b - z_c)$ with $2p_y$ will be called $S(\sigma_y)$. A *direct* σ overlap, such as the overlap between z_a and $2p_x$ (Fig. 4–8), will be called $S(p_\sigma, p_\sigma)$. To evaluate $S(\sigma_x)$ and $S(\sigma_y)$ in terms of $S(p_\sigma, p_\sigma)$, we use the following calculations:

$$S(\sigma_x) = \sqrt{\tfrac{2}{3}} \int (2p_x)(z_a - \tfrac{1}{2}z_b - \tfrac{1}{2}z_c)\, d\tau$$

$$= \sqrt{\tfrac{2}{3}}[S(p_\sigma,\ p_\sigma) + \tfrac{1}{2}\cos 60° S(p_\sigma,\ p_\sigma) + \tfrac{1}{2}\cos 60° S(p_\sigma,\ p_\sigma)]$$

$$= \sqrt{\tfrac{2}{3}}(\tfrac{3}{2})[S(p_\sigma,\ p_\sigma)] = \sqrt{\tfrac{3}{2}}S(p_\sigma,\ p_\sigma) \tag{4–11}$$

$$S(\sigma_y) = \frac{1}{\sqrt{2}}\int (2p_y)(z_b - z_c)\, d\tau$$

$$= \frac{1}{\sqrt{2}}[\cos 30°\ S(p_\sigma,\ p_\sigma) + \cos 30°\ S(p_\sigma,\ p_\sigma)]$$

$$= \frac{1}{\sqrt{2}}\left(\frac{\sqrt{3}}{2} + \frac{\sqrt{3}}{2}\right)[S(p_\sigma,\ p_\sigma)] = \sqrt{\tfrac{3}{2}}S(p_\sigma,\ p_\sigma) \tag{4–12}$$

Since the overlaps are the same in σ_x and σ_y, and since the com-

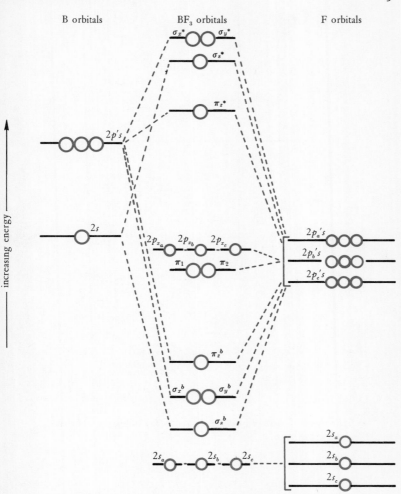

Figure 4–7   Relative orbital energies in BF₃.

bining boron and fluorine valence orbitals have the same initial
energies, it follows that σ_x and σ_y are degenerate in trigonal-planar
molecules.   However, it is worth pointing out that σ_x and σ_y are not
necessarily degenerate if the bond angles deviate from 120°.

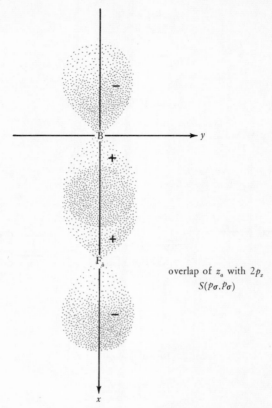

overlap of z_a with $2p_x$

$S(p\sigma.p\sigma)$

Figure 4-8   Standard two-atom σ overlap between p orbitals.

4–6   GROUND STATE OF BF₃

There are 24 valence electrons in BF₃ [7 from each fluorine $(2s^2 2p^5)$, 3 from the boron $(2s^2 2p)$]. Placing these electrons in the most stable molecular orbitals, we obtain a ground-state configuration:

$$(2s_a)^2(2s_b)^2(2s_c)^2(\sigma_s{}^b)^2(\sigma_x{}^b)^2(\sigma_y{}^b)^2(\pi_z{}^b)^2(\pi_1)^2(\pi_2)^2(2p_{x_a})^2(2p_{x_b})^2(2p_{x_c})^2$$

$$S = 0$$

There are six electrons in σ^b orbitals to give a total of three σ bonds for BF₃; in addition, the two electrons the $\pi_z{}^b$ orbital indicate one π

bond. The B—F bond length in BF_3 is 1.291 A; the B—F bond energy is 154 kcal/mole.

4–7 VALENCE BONDS FOR BF_3

The valence-bond description of the ground state of BF_3 is comparable to the molecular-orbital description. Three equivalent sp^2 hybrid orbitals are formed first by mixing together the $2s$, $2p_x$, and $2p_y$ boron orbitals, as shown in Fig. 4–9. Each sp^2 hybrid orbital has one-third s and two-thirds p character. These three sp^2 orbitals are then used to make three electron-pair σ bonds with the $2p_z$ fluorine orbitals. In addition, the $2p_z$ boron orbital can be used to make a π bond with any one of the three fluorine $2p_y$ orbitals. Thus there are three equivalent resonance structures for BF_3, as shown in Fig. 4–10. Notice that the three resonance structures move the electron-pair π bond around the "ring"; this is analogous to having two electrons in the delocalized π_z^b molecular orbital.

PROBLEM

4–1. Construct the wave functions for the three equivalent sp^2 hybrid orbitals.

Solution. It is convenient to use the coordinate system shown in Fig. 4–1, directing the three sp^2 hybrid orbitals at atoms a, b, and c. The s, p_x, and p_y orbitals are used to form the sp^2 orbitals. Each hybrid orbital has one-third s character. Of the two p orbitals, only the p_x is used to bond with atom a (p_y has zero overlap with a). Since each sp^2 orbital has two-thirds p character, the wave function for sp_a^2 is

$$\psi(sp_a^2) = \sqrt{\tfrac{1}{3}}s + \sqrt{\tfrac{2}{3}}p_x$$

The remaining third of the p_x orbital is divided equally between b and c. Since the p_y orbital has not been used as yet, and since it overlaps equally well with b and c, we split it up between b and c to complete the two-thirds p character in sp_b^2 and sp_c^2. Choosing the algebraic signs in the functions so that large and equal lobes are directed at b and c, we have:

$$\psi(sp_b^2) = \sqrt{\tfrac{1}{3}}s - \sqrt{\tfrac{1}{6}}p_x + \sqrt{\tfrac{1}{2}}p_y$$

$$\psi(sp_c^2) = \sqrt{\tfrac{1}{3}}s - \sqrt{\tfrac{1}{6}}p_x - \sqrt{\tfrac{1}{2}}p_y$$

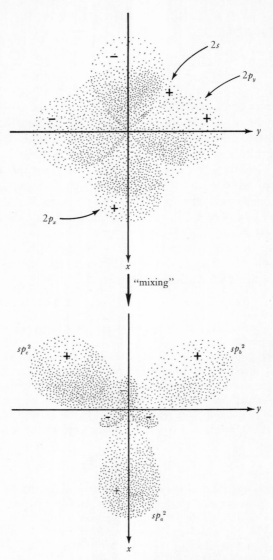

Figure 4–9   Formation of three sp^2 hybrid orbitals.

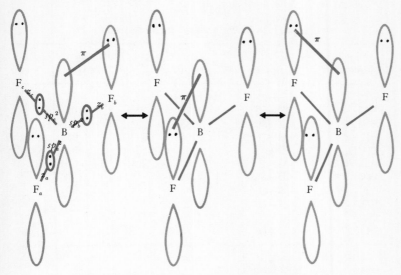

Figure 4–10 **Valence-bond structures for BF₃.**

The boundary surfaces of $sp_a{}^2$, $sp_b{}^2$, and $sp_c{}^2$ are shown in Fig. 4–9. Bonding orbitals are combinations of the sp^2 orbitals and appropriate σ orbitals of atoms a, b, and c:

$$\Psi_a = c_1\psi(sp_a{}^2) + c_2z_a$$

$$\Psi_b = c_1\psi(sp_b{}^2) + c_2z_b$$

$$\Psi_c = c_1\psi(sp_c{}^2) + c_2z_c$$

4–8   OTHER TRIGONAL-PLANAR MOLECULES

Elements in the boron family are the central atoms in many trigonal-planar molecules. Also, several important molecules and complex ions containing oxygen have trigonal-planar structures, among them SO_3, $NO_3{}^-$, and $CO_3{}^{2-}$. Bond properties of a number of trigonal-planar molecules are given in Table 4–1. The BH_3 molecule, which is presumably trigonal planar, is more stable in a dimeric form,

Table 4-1
Properties of Trigonal-Planar Molecules[a]

Molecule	Bond	Bond length, A	Bond energy (BE), kcal/mole
BF_3	B—F	1.291	154
BCl_3	B—Cl	1.74	109
BBr_3	B—Br	1.87	90
BH_3	B—H		93
$B(CH_3)_3$	B—C	1.56	89
$Al(CH_3)_3$	Al—C		61
$B(OR)_3$[b]	B—OR	1.38	128
SO_3	S—O	1.43	104
NO_3^-	N—O	1.22	
CO_3^{2-}	C—O	1.29	
BO_3^{3-}	B—O	1.38	

[a]Data from T. L. Cottrell, *The Strengths of Chemical Bonds*, Butterworths, London, 1958, Table 11.5.1.
[b]R = CH_3 or C_2H_5; R = H, 1.36A.

$$BH_3 + BH_3 \rightarrow B_2H_6$$

The bonding in *diborane* B_2H_6 is described in a number of other sources.[1]

The $B(CH_3)_3$ and $Al(CH_3)_3$ molecules have trigonal-planar parts.

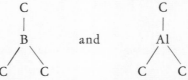

The structure around each carbon is tetrahedral, as will be described in Chapter V.

[1] See, for example, F. A. Cotton and G. Wilkinson, *Advanced Inorganic Chemistry*, Wiley-Interscience, New York, 1962, pp. 200–203; W. N. Lipscomb, *Boron Hydrides*, Benjamin, New York, 1963, Chap. 2; C. J. Ballhausen and H. B. Gray, *Introductory Notes on Molecular-Orbital Theory*, Benjamin, New York, 1965, Chap. 7.

SUPPLEMENTARY PROBLEMS

1. In most cases it is convenient to have a normalized linear combination of orbitals to bond with a central atom. For example, the combination appropriate for $2s$ in a trigonal-planar molecule is $(z_a + z_b + z_c)$. The normalized combination is $\dfrac{1}{\sqrt{3}}(z_a + z_b + z_c)$. Normalize the combinations $(z_b - z_c)$ and $(z_a - \frac{1}{2}z_b - \frac{1}{2}z_c)$.

2. Show that the molecular-orbital and valence-bond descriptions of σ bonding in a trigonal-planar molecule are equivalent, if, in Eqs. (4–1), (4–3), and (4–5), $C_1 = C_5 = C_9$ and $C = \sqrt{3}C_2 = \sqrt{2}C_6 = \sqrt{\frac{3}{2}}C_{10}$. In general, do you expect that $C_1 = C_5$? $C_5 = C_9$? $\sqrt{3}C_2 = \sqrt{2}C_6$? $\sqrt{2}C_6 = \sqrt{\frac{3}{2}}C_{10}$? Explain.

V

Tetrahedral Molecules

5–1 CH₄

The methane molecule, CH_4, has a tetrahedral structure. This structure is shown in Fig. 5–1. With the carbon in the center of the cube, the hydrogens are then placed at opposite corners of the cube, as defined by a regular tetrahedron. The origin of the rectangular coordinate system is chosen at the center of the cube, with the $x, y,$ and z axes perpendicular to the faces. All the carbon valence orbitals, $2s, 2p_x, 2p_y,$ and $2p_z$, must be used to form an adequate set of σ molecular orbitals.

The overlap of the four $1s$ hydrogen orbitals with the carbon $2s$ orbital is shown in Fig. 5–2. The linear combination $(1s_a + 1s_b + 1s_c + 1s_d)$ is appropriate. The bonding and antibonding molecular orbitals are:

$$\psi(\sigma_s{}^b) = C_1 2s + C_2(1s_a + 1s_b + 1s_c + 1s_d) \qquad (5\text{–}1)$$

$$\psi(\sigma_s{}^*) = C_3 2s - C_4(1s_a + 1s_b + 1s_c + 1s_d) \qquad (5\text{–}2)$$

The overlap of the four $1s$ orbitals with the carbon $2p_z$ orbital is shown in Fig. 5–3. Hydrogen orbitals $1s_a$ and $1s_b$ overlap the plus lobe, and orbitals $1s_c$ and $1s_d$ overlap the minus lobe. Thus the proper combination is $(1s_a + 1s_b - 1s_c - 1s_d)$.

120

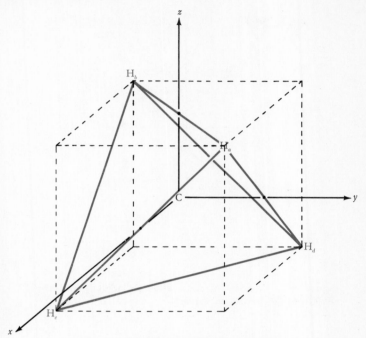

Figure 5–1 Coordinate system for CH$_4$.

The $2p_x$ and $2p_y$ carbon orbitals overlap the four hydrogen orbitals in the same way as $2p_z$. This is shown in Fig. 5–4. The linear combinations are $(1s_a + 1s_d - 1s_b - 1s_c)$ with $2p_y$, and $(1s_a + 1s_c - 1s_b - 1s_d)$ with $2p_x$. The molecular orbitals are given below.

$$\psi(\sigma_z{}^b) = C_5 2p_z + C_6(1s_a + 1s_b - 1s_c - 1s_d) \tag{5-3}$$

$$\psi(\sigma_z{}^*) = C_7 2p_z - C_8(1s_a + 1s_b - 1s_c - 1s_d) \tag{5-4}$$

$$\psi(\sigma_y{}^b) = C_9 2p_y + C_{10}(1s_a + 1s_d - 1s_b - 1s_c) \tag{5-5}$$

$$\psi(\sigma_y{}^*) = C_{11} 2p_y - C_{12}(1s_a + 1s_d - 1s_b - 1s_c) \tag{5-6}$$

$$\psi(\sigma_x{}^b) = C_{13} 2p_x + C_{14}(1s_a + 1s_c - 1s_b - 1s_d) \tag{5-7}$$

$$\psi(\sigma_x{}^*) = C_{15} 2p_x - C_{16}(1s_a + 1s_c - 1s_b - 1s_d) \tag{5-8}$$

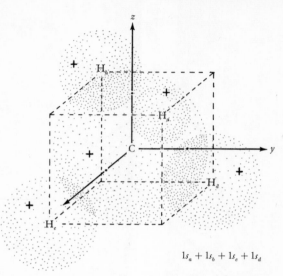

$$1s_a + 1s_b + 1s_c + 1s_d$$

Figure 5–2 Overlap of the carbon 2s orbital with the 1s orbitals of the hydrogen atoms.

5–2   GROUND STATE OF CH_4

The molecular-orbital energy-level scheme for CH_4 is shown in Fig. 5–5. The σ_x, σ_y, and σ_z orbitals have the same overlap in a tetrahedral molecule and are degenerate in energy. This is clear from the overlaps shown in Figs. 5–3 and 5–4.

There are eight valence electrons in CH_4 because carbon is $2s^2 2p^2$ and each of the four hydrogens contributes a $1s$ electron. Thus the ground state is

$$(\sigma_s^b)^2(\sigma_x^b)^2(\sigma_y^b)^2(\sigma_z^b)^2 \qquad S = 0$$

There are four σ bonds in CH_4. The average C—H bond energy is 99.3 kcal/mole. The C—H bond length in CH_4 is 1.093 A.

5–3   THE TETRAHEDRAL ANGLE

The H—C—H bond angle in CH_4 is 109°28′. We can calculate the tetrahedral angle by simple trigonometry. First, we place the CH_4

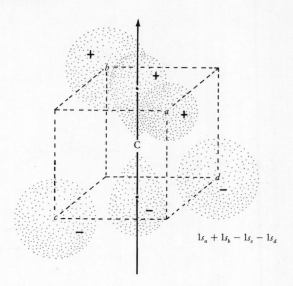

$$1s_a + 1s_b - 1s_c - 1s_d$$

Figure 5-3 Overlap of the carbon $2p_z$ orbital with the $1s$ orbitals of the hydrogen atoms.

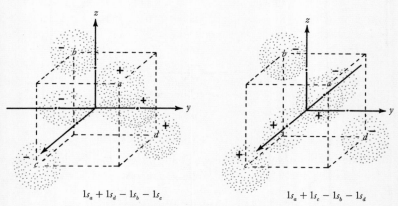

$$1s_a + 1s_d - 1s_b - 1s_c \qquad\qquad 1s_a + 1s_c - 1s_b - 1s_d$$

Figure 5-4 Overlap of the carbon $2p_x$ and $2p_y$ orbitals with the $1s$ orbitals of the hydrogen atoms.

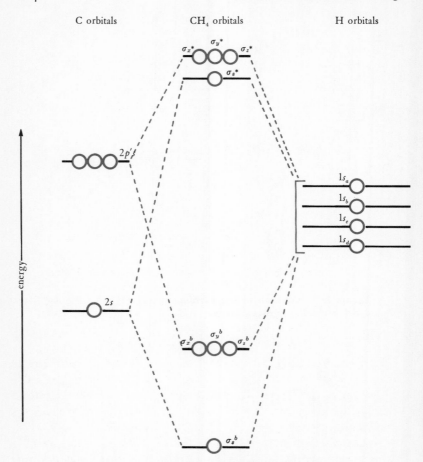

Figure 5-5   Relative orbital energies in CH₄.

molecule in a unit cube, as shown in Fig. 5–6. The lengths of the sides defining the H_a—C—H_d angle θ are obtained by using the Pythagorean theorem.   Thus we have the result

$$\cos \frac{\theta}{2} = \frac{\sqrt{3}}{3} \qquad \text{or} \qquad \theta = 109°28' \qquad (5\text{–}9)$$

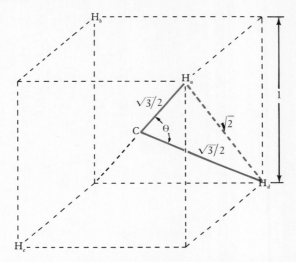

Figure 5–6 Unit-cube model for evaluating the tetrahedral angle.

5–4 VALENCE BONDS FOR CH₄

Four equivalent valence orbitals centered on carbon can be constructed by scrambling together the $2s$, $2p_x$, $2p_y$, and $2p_z$ orbitals. These equivalent orbitals are called sp^3 hybrids, and their construction is shown schematically in Fig. 5–7. Each sp^3 hybrid orbital has one-fourth s character and three-fourths p character.

The four sp^3 orbitals are directed toward the corners of a regular tetrahedron, and thus are ideally suited for forming four localized bonding orbitals with the four hydrogen $1s$ orbitals. The valence-bond structure for CH_4 is shown in Fig. 5–8.

PROBLEM

5–1. The normalized wave functions for the four equivalent sp^3 hybrid orbitals are listed below (coordinate system as shown in Fig. 5–7):

$$\psi(sp_a{}^3) = \tfrac{1}{2}s + \sqrt{\tfrac{3}{4}}(p_x + p_y + p_z)$$

$$\psi(sp_b{}^3) = \tfrac{1}{2}s + \sqrt{\tfrac{3}{4}}(-p_x - p_y + p_z)$$

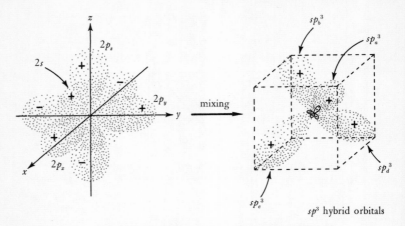

Figure 5–7   Formation of four sp^3 hybrid orbitals.

$$\psi(sp_c{}^3) = \tfrac{1}{2}s + \sqrt{\tfrac{3}{4}}(p_x - p_y - p_z)$$

$$\psi(sp_d{}^3) = \tfrac{1}{2}s + \sqrt{\tfrac{3}{4}}(-p_x + p_y - p_z)$$

Show how these orbitals are obtained by following the procedure used to solve Problem 4–1.

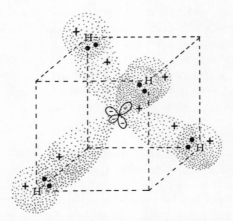

Figure 5–8   Valence-bond structure for CH_4.

5-5 OTHER TETRAHEDRAL MOLECULES

Members of the carbon family (carbon, silicon, germanium, tin, and lead) readily form four σ bonds with four adjacent atoms. The resulting molecules invariably have a tetrahedral structure around

Table 5-1

Properties of Tetrahedral Molecules[a]

Molecule	Bond	Bond length, A	Bond energy (BE), kcal/mole
CH_4	CH_3-H	1.093	101(DE)
	$C-H$		99.3
CF_4	$C-F$	1.36	116
CCl_4	$C-Cl$	1.761	78.2
CBr_4	CBr_3-Br	1.942	<50(DE)
SiH_4	$Si-H$	1.480	76
SiF_4	$Si-F$	1.54	135
$SiCl_4$	$Si-Cl$	2.02	91
$SiBr_4$	$Si-Br$	2.15	74
SiI_4	$Si-I$	2.43	56
$Si(CH_3)_4$	$Si-C$	1.93	72
$Si(C_2H_5)_4$	$Si-C$		60
$GeCl_4$	$Ge-Cl$	2.08	81
$GeBr_4$	$Ge-Br$	2.32	66
GeI_4	$Ge-I$	2.48	51
$SnCl_4$	$Sn-Cl$	2.30	76
$SnBr_4$	$Sn-Br$		65
$Sn(CH_3)_4$	$Sn-C$	2.18	
$Sn(C_2H_5)_4$	$Sn-C$		54
$Pb(CH_3)_4$	$Pb-C$	2.30	
$Pb(C_2H_5)_4$	$-C$		31
SO_4^{2-}	O	1.49	
ClO_4^-	O	1.44	
NH_4^+	$N-H$	1.03	
BH_4^-	$B-H$	1.22	
BF_4^-	$B-F$	1.43	

[a]Data from T. L. Cottrell, *The Strengths of Chemical Bonds*, Butterworths, London, 1958, Table 11.5.1.

the central atom. The bonding in these molecules involves the use
of one s and three p valence orbitals by the central atom, and of an
appropriate valence orbital by each of the four surrounding atoms.

A number of important oxyanions have a tetrahedral structure,
among them SO_4^{2-} and ClO_4^-. Properties of a representative group
of tetrahedral molecules are given in Table 5–1.

SUPPLEMENTARY PROBLEMS

1. Describe the bonding in CF_4 in terms of molecular orbitals, and
construct a molecular-orbital energy-level diagram.   Around which
nucleus or nuclei do the electrons spend more time in the σ^b orbitals?
Do you expect any partial ionic character in the C—F bonds? What
is the dipole moment of CF_4? Why?

2. Under what conditions are the molecular-orbital and valence-
bond descriptions of bonding in CH_4 the same?   From Eqs. (5–1),
(5–3), (5–5), and (5–7), construct the valence-bond bonding functions that are shown in Fig. 5–8.

3. What is the structure of BH_4^-? of NH_4^+? Are the CH_4 orbitals
appropriate for these molecules? Discuss the partial ionic character
you might expect in the B—H, C—H, and N—H bonds. Make an
estimate of the coefficients in Eqs. (5–1) through (5–8) that might
be expected for the BH_4^-, CH_4, and NH_4^+ molecules.

VI

Trigonal-Pyramidal Molecules

6–1 NH$_3$

A familiar example of a trigonal-pyramidal molecule is ammonia, NH$_3$. The NH$_3$ molecule is shown in Fig. 6–1. The three hydrogens, which are bent out of the x,y plane, form the base of a trigonal pyramid that has the nitrogen at the apex. Each N—H makes an angle θ with z. In addition, N—H$_a$ is lined up with the x axis, and N—H$_b$ and N—H$_c$ make 30° angles with $+y$ and $-y$, respectively. Thus NH$_3$ is aligned the same way we aligned a trigonal-planar molecule (Fig. 4–1), but with the three peripheral atoms bent down.

Bonding in NH$_3$ involves the hydrogen $1s$ valence orbitals and the nitrogen $2s$ and $2p$ valence orbitals. Let us ignore the $2s$ nitrogen orbital for the moment, and consider only the $2p$–$1s$ bonding.

The overlap of the three hydrogen $1s$ orbitals with the nitrogen $2p_z$ orbital is shown in Fig. 6–2. The correct combination of $1s$ orbitals is $(1s_a + 1s_b + 1s_c)$. The σ_z molecular orbitals are:

$$\psi(\sigma_z{}^b) = C_1 2p_z + C_2(1s_a + 1s_b + 1s_c) \qquad (6\text{–}1)$$

$$\psi(\sigma_z{}^*) = C_3 2p_z - C_4(1s_a + 1s_b + 1s_c) \qquad (6\text{–}2)$$

The overlap of $2p_y$ with $1s_b$ and $1s_c$ is shown in Fig. 6–3. The correct combination is $(1s_b - 1s_c)$. The σ_y molecular orbitals are:

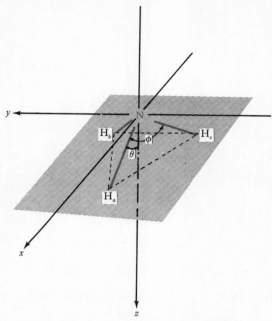

Figure 6-1   Coordinate system for NH₃.

$$\psi(\sigma_y{}^b) = C_5 2p_y + C_6(1s_b - 1s_c) \tag{6-3}$$

$$\psi(\sigma_y{}^*) = C_7 2p_y - C_8(1s_b - 1s_c) \tag{6-4}$$

The overlap of $2p_x$ with $1s_a$, $1s_b$, and $1s_c$ is shown in Fig. 6–4. Since $1s_b$ and $1s_c$ make an angle of $60°$ with $-x$, the overlap of $1s_b$ or $1s_c$ with $2p_x$ is only one-half ($\cos 60° = \frac{1}{2}$) that of $1s_a$ with $2p_x$ (see Section 4–2). Thus the proper $1s$ combination is $(1s_a - \frac{1}{2} 1s_b - \frac{1}{2} 1s_c)$. The σ_x molecular orbitals are:

$$\psi(\sigma_x{}^b) = C_9 2p_x + C_{10}(1s_a - \tfrac{1}{2} 1s_b - \tfrac{1}{2} 1s_c) \tag{6-5}$$

$$\psi(\sigma_x{}^*) = C_{11} 2p_x - C_{12}(1s_a - \tfrac{1}{2} 1s_b - \tfrac{1}{2} 1s_c) \tag{6-6}$$

6–2   OVERLAP IN σ_x, σ_y, AND σ_z

A calculation of the overlap in the σ_x, σ_y, and σ_z molecular orbitals is easily carried out. The direct overlap of a $2p$ with a $1s$ valence

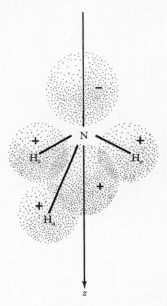

$$2p_z + 1s_a + 1s_b + 1s_c$$

Figure 6-2 Overlap of the nitrogen $2p_z$ orbital with the $1s$ orbitals of the hydrogen atoms.

orbital is shown in Fig. 6–5; this we shall denote as $S(1s,2p_\sigma)$. We then proceed to express the molecular-orbital overlaps in terms of $S(1s,2p_\sigma)$:

$$S(\sigma_z) = \int 2p_z \frac{1}{\sqrt{3}}(1s_a + 1s_b + 1s_c)\, d\tau$$

$$= \frac{1}{\sqrt{3}}[\cos\theta\, S(1s,2p_\sigma) + \cos\theta\, S(1s,\,2p_\sigma) + \cos\theta\, S(1s,2p_\sigma)]$$

$$= \sqrt{3}\cos\theta\, S(1s,2p_\sigma) \tag{6–7}$$

$$S(\sigma_y) = \int 2p_y \frac{1}{\sqrt{2}}(1s_b - 1s_c)\, d\tau$$

$$= \frac{1}{\sqrt{2}}[\cos 30°\sin\theta\, S(1s,2p_\sigma) + \cos 30°\sin\theta\, S(1s,2p_\sigma)]$$

$$= \sqrt{\tfrac{3}{2}}\sin\theta\, S(1s,2p_\sigma) \tag{6–8}$$

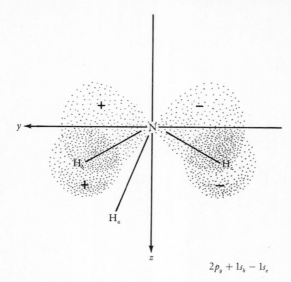

$$2p_y + 1s_b - 1s_c$$

Figure 6–3 Overlap of the nitrogen $2p_y$ orbital with the 1s orbitals of the hydrogen atoms.

$$S(\sigma_x) = \int 2p_x \sqrt{\tfrac{2}{3}}(1s_a - \tfrac{1}{2}1s_b - \tfrac{1}{2}1s_c)\,d\tau$$

$$= \sqrt{\tfrac{2}{3}}[\sin\theta\,S(1s,2p_\sigma) + \cos 60° \sin\theta\,S(1s,2p_\sigma) + \cos 60° \sin\theta$$
$$\times S(1s,2p_\sigma)]$$

$$= \sqrt{\tfrac{3}{2}}\sin\theta\,S(1s,2p_\sigma) \tag{6–9}$$

It is important to note from Eqs. (6–7), (6–8), and (6–9) that σ_y and σ_x are equivalent, and therefore their energies will be the same for any value of θ. When $\theta = 90°$, of course, we obtain the correct overlap values for a trigonal-planar molecule (see Section 4–5):

$$S(\sigma_z) = 0$$

$$S(\sigma_y) = S(\sigma_x) = \sqrt{\tfrac{3}{2}}S(1s,2p_\sigma)$$

Let us now investigate the case for an H—N—H bond angle of 90° ($\phi = 90°$ in Fig. 6–1). Calling the N—H_a length unity, the other pertinent distances given in Fig. 6–6 can be easily obtained by geom-

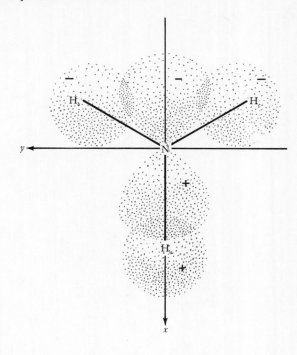

$$2p_x + 1s_a - 1s_b - 1s_c$$

Figure 6-4 Overlap of the nitrogen $2p_x$ orbital with the 1s orbitals of the hydrogen atoms.

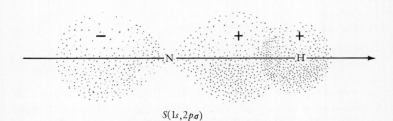

$$S(1s, 2p\sigma)$$

Figure 6-5 Standard two-atom σ overlap between an s and a p orbital.

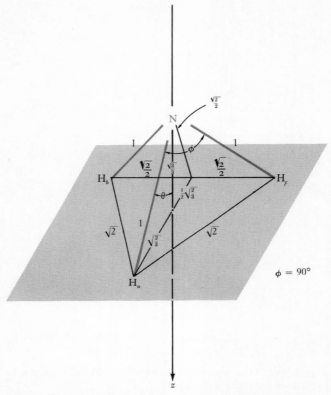

Figure 6-6 Relative distances in the NH₃ molecule for an H N H bond angle of 90°.

etry. We see that for $\phi = 90°$, $\cos \theta = \dfrac{\sqrt{3}}{3}$ and $\sin \theta = \sqrt{\tfrac{2}{3}}$. Thus, Eqs. (6–7), (6–8), and (6–9) reduce to

$$S(\sigma_z) = S(\sigma_y) = S(\sigma_x) = S(1s, 2p_\sigma) \qquad (6\text{--}10)$$

In other words, the σ_x, σ_y, and σ_z molecular orbitals are the same for $\phi = 90°$. This is no surprise, since the $2p_x$, $2p_y$, and $2p_z$ orbitals make 90° angles with each other, and for $\phi = 90°$ the $1s$ orbitals can be aligned along the x, y, and z axes, as shown in Fig. 6–7. Each hydro-

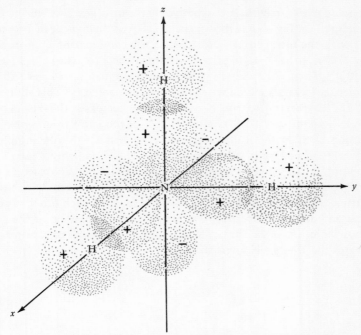

Figure 6–7 Simple picture of the bonding in NH₃, using only the nitrogen 2p orbitals.

gen overlaps one $2p$ orbital, as in Eq. (6–10). The total overlap in σ_x, σ_y, and σ_z is smaller for any other angle.

6–3 THE INTERELECTRONIC REPULSIONS AND H—N—H BOND ANGLE IN NH₃

The actual H—N—H bond angle in NH_3 is 107°, or 17° larger than the angle predicted for pure $2p$–$1s$ bonding. It is probable that the mutual repulsions of the one nonbonding pair (called a *lone pair*) and the three bonding pairs of electrons are responsible for the 17° angle opening. The four electron pairs must therefore be so arranged as to minimize these interelectronic repulsions. One way to get the three bonding pairs farther apart is to involve the nitrogen $2s$ orbital in the bonding. In Fig. 6–8 is shown the overlap of the hydrogen $1s$ orbitals with the nitrogen $2s$. Notice that the combination appropriate for $2s$ $(1s_a + 1s_b + 1s_c)$ is the $1s$ combination in σ_z [Eqs. (6–1) and (6–2)]. Thus σ_s "mixes together" with $\sigma_z{}^b$ and $\sigma_z{}^*$ to give three molecular orbitals which we shall call $\sigma_s{}^b$, σ_z, and $\sigma_z{}^*$. This addition of $2s$ "character" to the N—H bonding increases the H—N—H angle from 90° to 107°. You may think of the angle opening by inclusion of $2s$ in the following way: The best H—N—H angle for "pure" $2p$ bonding is 90°. The best H—N—H angle for "pure" $2s$ bonding is 120°, since the symmetrical trigonal planar structure allows the best overlap arrangement for three hydrogen $1s$ orbitals with a $2s$ orbital. (The $1s$ orbitals are as far from each other as possible and do not compete for overlap of the same portion of the $2s$.) Thus inclusion of $2s$ character in a "pure" $2p$-bonding scheme increases the H—N—H angle from 90°.

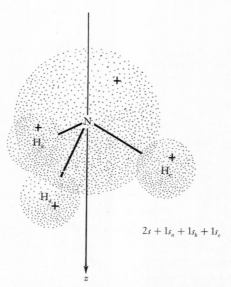

$$2s + 1s_a + 1s_b + 1s_c$$

Figure 6–8 Overlap of the nitrogen 2s orbital with the 1s orbitals of the hydrogen atoms.

The similar valence-bond idea, particularly appealing, is that the bonding pairs and the lone pair are in four tetrahedral sp^3 orbitals. This structure places the four electron pairs as far away from each other as possible. The "tetrahedral" structure of NH_3 is shown in Fig. 6–9. The slight deviation of the H—N—H bond angle from the tetrahedral angle of 109° is considered a result of the nonequivalence of the bonding and non-bonding pairs of electrons.

6–4 BOND ANGLES OF OTHER TRIGONAL-PYRAMIDAL MOLECULES

The H—P—H and H—As—H angles in PH_3 and AsH_3 are 94° and 92°, respectively. This probably indicates a high degree of phosphorus and arsenic p-orbital character in the three bonding orbitals. We assume that the mutual repulsions of bonding pairs of electrons are reduced in going from nitrogen to phosphorus to arsenic. This is a reasonable assumption, since we know from atomic spectra that the atomic interelectronic repulsions, in the valence p orbitals, decrease in the order $N > P > As$. The trihalides of nitrogen, phosphorus, arsenic, antimony, and bismuth are trigonal pyramidal. The bond angles are all in the 95 to 105° range, as given in Table 6–1.

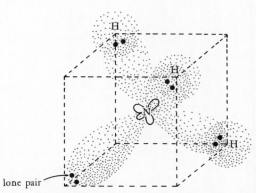

Figure 6–9 Valence-bond structure for NH_3, using sp^3 orbitals for nitrogen.

Table 6-1
Properties of Trigonal-Pyramidal Molecules[a]

AB_3 molecule	$B—A—B$ angle, deg	AB bond length, A	AB bond energy (BE), kcal/mole
NH_3	107	1.014	93.4
NF_3	103	1.37	65
NCl_3			46
PH_3	94	1.42	77
PF_3	104		117
PCl_3	100	2.04	78
PBr_3	100	2.20	63
PI_3		2.47	44
AsH_3	92	1.52	59
AsF_3	102	1.71	111
$AsCl_3$	98	2.16	70
$AsBr_3$		2.33	58
AsI_3		2.54	43
$SbCl_3$	104	2.48	67
$BiCl_3$		2.48	67
$Bi(CH_3)_3$		2.30	31

[a]Data from T. L. Cottrell, *The Strengths of Chemical Bonds*, Butterworths, London, 1958, Table 11.5.1; L. E. Sutton (ed.), "Interatomic Distances," *Special Publication No. 11*, The Chemical Society, London, 1958.

6-5 GROUND STATE OF NH_3

The molecular-orbital energy-level scheme for NH_3 is shown in Fig. 6–10. The σ_x and σ_y orbitals are degenerate. The eight valence electrons give a ground-state configuration of

$$(\sigma_s{}^b)^2(\sigma_x{}^b)^2(\sigma_y{}^b)^2(\sigma_z)^2 \qquad S = 0$$

There are three σ bonds. The N—H bond length is 1.014 A, and the average N—H bond energy is 93.4 kcal/mole. The electrons in the bonding orbitals spend more time around nitrogen than around the hydrogens. This means that in the ground state the nitrogen has a small negative charge and the hydrogens carry a small positive charge. Thus there are three *bond dipoles*, as shown in Fig. 6–11. These three bond dipoles add vectorially to give NH_3 a net dipole

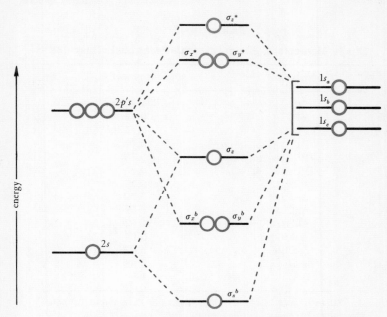

Figure 6-10   Relative orbital energies in NH₃.

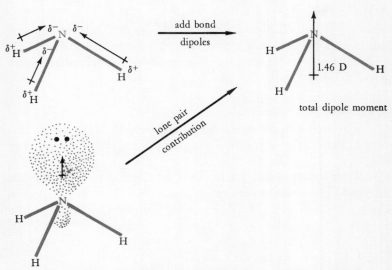

Figure 6-11   Contributions to the dipole moment of NH₃.

Table 6-2

Dipole Moments of Some Trigonal-Pyramidal Molecules[a]

Molecule	Dipole moment, D
NH_3	1.47
NF_3	0.23
PH_3	0.55
PF_3	1.03
PCl_3	0.79
PBr_3	0.61
AsH_3	0.15
AsF_3	2.82
$AsCl_3$	1.99
$AsBr_3$	1.67
AsI_3	0.97
$SbCl_3$	3.93
$SbBr_3$	2.48
SbI_3	1.59

[a]Data from A. L. McClellan, *Tables of Experimental Dipole Moments*, Freeman, San Francisco, 1963.

moment. The total dipole moment, 1.46 D, also includes a contribution from the lone-pair electrons in σ_z, as indicated in Fig. 6–11.

Dipole moments for a number of trigonal-pyramidal molecules are given in Table 6–2.

SUPPLEMENTARY PROBLEMS

1. Why is the dipole moment of NH_3 larger than the dipole moment of PH_3? Why is the dipole moment of PF_3 larger than that of PCl_3?

2. What structure would you expect for CH_3^- and H_3O^+. Discuss the bonding in these molecules.

VII

Angular Triatomic Molecules

7–1 H_2O

The most familiar angular triatomic molecule is water, H_2O. The H—O—H bond angle in the water molecule is known to be 105°. We can conveniently derive the molecular orbitals for H_2O by placing the oxygen atom at the origin of an xyz coordinate system. The two hydrogens are placed in the x,z plane, as shown in Fig. 7–1. Imagine starting with a linear H—O—H along the z axis and bending the two hydrogens toward the x axis, until the H—O—H angle θ corresponds to the observed 105°. It is convenient to bend each hydrogen the same amount from the z axis, so that the x axis bisects θ. We can go through this procedure for any angular triatomic molecule, independent of the value of θ. Thus the σ molecular orbitals for H_2O are a representative set.

The valence orbitals involved are $2s$ and $2p$ for oxygen and $1s$ for hydrogen. The overlaps of the $2p$ orbitals with the two hydrogen $1s$ orbitals are shown in Fig. 7–2. From these overlaps, we can write the following set of wave functions:

$$\psi(\sigma_x{}^b) = C_1 2p_x + C_2(1s_a + 1s_b) \qquad (7\text{–}1)$$

$$\psi(\sigma_x{}^*) = C_3 2p_x - C_4(1s_a + 1s_b) \qquad (7\text{–}2)$$

$$\psi(\sigma_z{}^b) = C_5 2p_z + C_6(1s_a - 1s_b) \qquad (7\text{–}3)$$

$$\psi(\sigma_z{}^*) = C_7 2p_z - C_8(1s_a - 1s_b) \qquad (7\text{–}4)$$

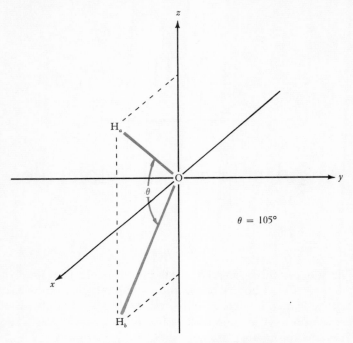

Figure 7–1   Coordinate system for H₂O.

The $2p_y$ oxygen orbital has no overlap with either $1s_a$ or $1s_b$, and thus it is nonbonding in our scheme. Notice that $2p_y$ is available for π bonding, but hydrogens do not have π valence orbitals.

The overlap of $2s$ with $1s_a$ and $1s_b$ is shown in Fig. 7–3. The combination $(1s_a + 1s_b)$, which was used in the σ_x orbitals, is correct for $2s$. This means that σ_s mixes with σ_x. The result is three molecular orbitals—a *bonding* orbital, an orbital that is *nearly nonbonding*, and an *antibonding* orbital. We shall call these orbitals σ_s^b, σ_x, and σ_x^*, respectively.

The molecular-orbital energy-level scheme is shown in Fig. 7–4, with the hydrogen $1s$ orbital placed above the oxygen $2s$ and $2p$ valence orbitals. The σ_z^b molecular orbital is seen to be more stable than the σ_x, owing to the interaction of σ_x with σ_s^b.

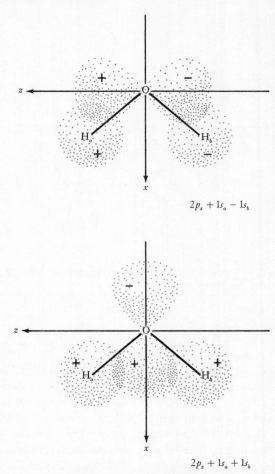

$$2p_z + 1s_a - 1s_b$$

$$2p_x + 1s_a + 1s_b$$

Figure 7–2 Overlap of the oxygen $2p_z$ and $2p_x$ orbitals with the 1s orbitals of the hydrogen atoms.

7–2 GROUND STATE OF H_2O

The ground-state electronic configuration of H_2O, with eight valence electrons (two from the hydrogens, $2s^2 2p^4$ or six from oxygen), is therefore

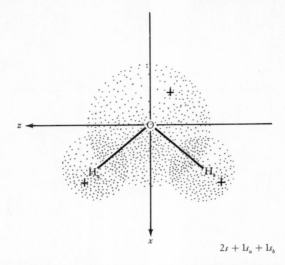

Figure 7–3 **Overlap of the oxygen 2s orbital with the 1s orbitals of the hydrogen atoms.**

$$(\sigma_s{}^b)^2(\sigma_z{}^b)^2(\sigma_x)^2(\pi_y)^2 \qquad S = 0$$

We note that all the electrons must be paired, and H_2O is diamagnetic. There are four electrons in σ^b orbitals, giving two σ bonds.

We might expect the H—O—H bond angle to be 90° if only the $2p_x$ and $2p_z$ orbitals were used in σ bonding. That is, a θ of 90° makes $2p_x$ and $2p_z$ equivalent with respect to overlap with the H valence orbitals. This is easy to see if we place the two hydrogens along the x and z axes, as shown in Fig. 7–5. The possibility of the $2s$ orbital being involved in bonding is one explanation for the 15° deviation of the H—O—H angle from 90°. To demonstrate the angle "opening," it is convenient (as for NH_3) to place the eight valence electrons into four sp^3 hybrid orbitals, as shown in Fig. 7–6. The fact that the H—O—H angle in water is less than 109° is, according to this view, a result of the different repulsions of electron pairs in bonding and nonbonding orbitals. The nonbonding pairs would repel each other more strongly than the bonding pairs, consistent with a 105° angle between the bonding pairs.

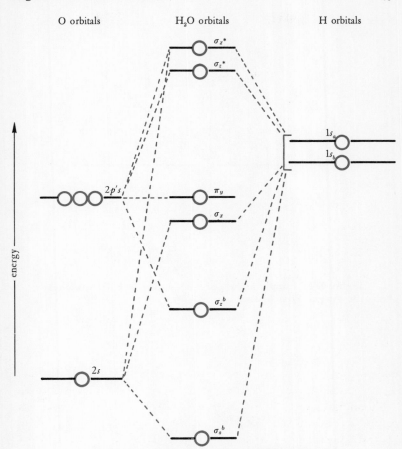

Figure 7-4 Relative orbital energies in H₂O.

The bond angle in H_2S is 92°, much closer to the 90° expected for pure p bonding. In H_2S, it is probable that there is strong $3p$–$1s$ bonding. This is consistent with the fact that the interelectronic repulsions in $3p$ orbitals on sulfur are known to be less than the interelectronic repulsions in $2p$ orbitals on oxygen.

The electrons in σ^b orbitals in H_2O spend more time near the oxygen than near the hydrogens, owing to the larger electronegativity of

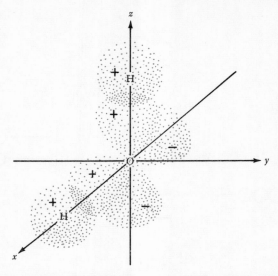

Figure 7–5 Simple picture of the bonding in H_2O, using only the oxygen $2p$ orbitals.

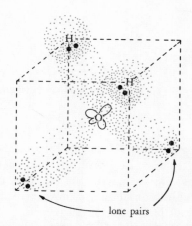

Figure 7–6 Valence-bond structure for H_2O, using sp^3 orbitals for oxygen.

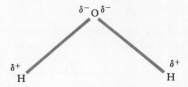

Figure 7-7   Separation of charge in H₂O in the ground state.

oxygen.   As a result, the hydrogens carry a small positive charge in the ground state of H_2O, as shown in Fig. 7-7.

The H_2O molecule has a dipole moment of 1.844 D.   The moment is due to the charge separation described above as well as to lone pairs, as shown in Fig. 7-8.   Each H—O bond has a small *bond dipole moment* resulting from the charge separation $\overset{\delta+}{H}$—$\overset{\delta-}{O}$.   Since the H_2O molecule is *angular*, these bond moments add together to give a resultant dipole moment.

Table 7-1 gives dipole moments of several angular triatomic molecules.

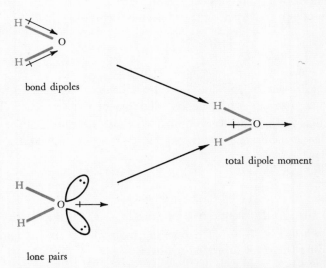

bond dipoles

total dipole moment

lone pairs

Figure 7-8   Contributions to the dipole moment of H₂O.

Table 7-1

Dipole Moments of Some Angular Triatomic Molecules[a]

Molecule	Dipole moment, D
H_2O	1.844
H_2S	0.92
SO_2	1.633
NO_2	0.39
O_3	0.52

[a]Data from A. L. McClellan, *Tables of Experimental Dipole Moments*, Freeman, San Francisco, 1963.

7–3   ANGULAR TRIATOMIC MOLECULES WITH π BONDING: NO_2

The NO_2 molecule is an example of an angular triatomic molecule with both σ and π bonding. We place the N of NO_2 at the origin of an xyz coordinate system shown in Fig. 7–9. The oxygens are situated in the x,z plane, bent away from the z axis. The O—N—O angle is θ. We shall consider the nitrogen $2s$ and $2p$ and the oxygen $2p$ orbitals in constructing the molecular orbitals.

7–4 σ ORBITALS

The nitrogen $2s$, $2p_x$, and $2p_z$ valence orbitals are used to form σ molecular orbitals with the $2p_{z_a}$ and $2p_{z_b}$ of the oxygens. The σ molecular orbitals are very similar to those we obtained for H_2O. In order of increasing energy, we have σ_s^b, σ_z^b, σ_x, σ_z^*, and σ_x^* (see Fig. 7–4).

7–5 π ORBITALS

The nitrogen $2p_y$ orbital overlaps the $2p_{y_a}$ and $2p_{y_b}$ on the oxygens, as shown in Fig. 7–10. The bonding molecular orbital is obtained by adding the three orbitals together:

$$\psi(\pi_y{}^b) = C_1 2p_y + C_2(y_a + y_b) \qquad (7\text{–}5)$$

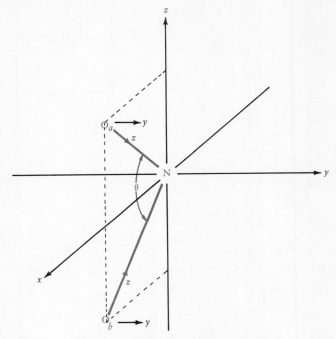

Figure 7-9 Coordinate system for NO₂.

The antibonding orbital has a node between O_a and N and between O_b and N:

$$\psi(\pi_y{}^*) = C_3 2p_y - C_4(y_a + y_b) \qquad (7\text{-}6)$$

The other combination of the $2p_y$ orbitals of O_a and O_b is $(2p_{y_a} - 2p_{y_b})$. This combination has zero net overlap with the nitrogen $2p_y$, and is the nonbonding molecular orbital:

$$\psi(\pi_y) = \frac{1}{\sqrt{2}}(y_a - y_b) \qquad (7\text{-}7)$$

We shall also consider the $2p_x$ orbitals of O_a and O_b nonbonding in NO_2. An approximate energy-level scheme for the molecular orbitals of NO_2 is given in Fig. 7-11.

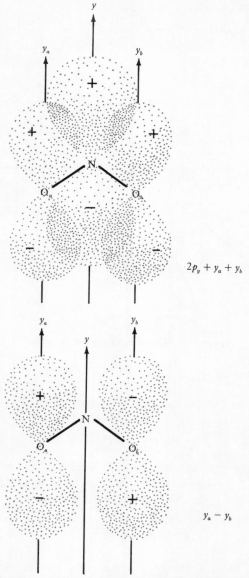

Figure 7–10   The π-orbital combinations in NO₂.

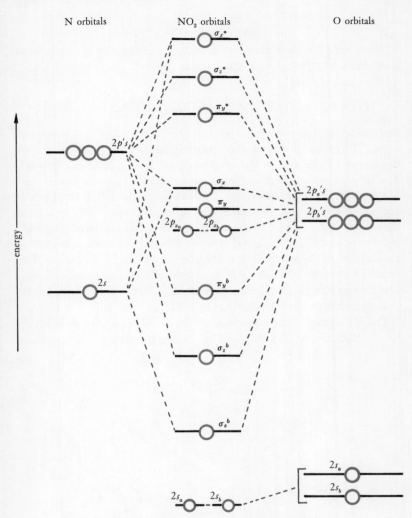

Figure 7–11 Relative orbital energies in NO₂.

7–6   GROUND STATE OF NO$_2$

There are 17 valence electrons in NO$_2$ (five from nitrogen, six from each oxygen) to place in the molecular orbitals given in Fig. 7–11. The ground state is

$$(2s_a)^2(2s_b)^2(\sigma_s{}^b)^2(\sigma_z{}^b)^2(\pi_y{}^b)^2(2p_{x_a})^2(2p_{x_b})^2(\pi_y)^2(\sigma_x) \qquad S = \tfrac{1}{2}$$

Since there is one unpaired electron, the NO$_2$ molecule is paramagnetic. Electron-spin resonance measurements have confirmed that the unpaired electron in the ground state of NO$_2$ is in a σ orbital. The ground-state electronic configuration gives two σ bonds and one π bond. It is instructive to compare the molecular-orbital bonding scheme with two possible equivalent valence-bond structures that can be written for NO$_2$ (see Fig. 7–12). The resonance between structures I and II spreads out the one π bond over the three atoms, an analogy to the π bonding molecular orbital (see Fig. 7–10). The unpaired electron is in an sp^2 hybrid orbital, which is similar to σ_x. The lone pair in the $2p_y$ system goes from O$_a$ to O$_b$, an analogy to the two electrons in the π_y molecular orbital (see Fig. 7–10).

The N—O bond length in NO$_2$ is 1.20 A. This compares with an N—O distance of 1.13 A in NO. The molecular-orbital bonding

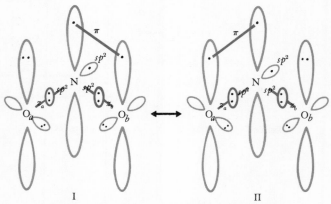

I   II

Figure 7–12   Valence-bond structures for NO$_2$.

Table 7-2

Properties of Angular Triatomic Molecules[a]

AB_2 molecule	$B-A-B$ angle, deg	Bond	Bond length, A	Bond energies, kcal/mole
H_2O	105	HO—H O—H	0.958	117.5(DE) 110.6(BE)
H_2S	92	H—SH H—S	1.334	90(DE) 83(BE)
H_2Se	91	H—Se	1.47	66(BE)
H_2Te	90	H—Te		57(BE)
HOCl	113	HO—Cl		60(DE)
HOBr		HO—Br		56(DE)
HOI		HO—I		56(DE)
OF_2	102	O—F	1.41	45.3(BE)
OCl_2	115	O—Cl	1.68	49(BE)
ClO_2	117	OCl—O Cl—O	1.484	57(DE) 60(BE)
BrO_2		O—BrO Br—O		70(DE) 60(BE)
NO_2	132	O—NO	1.20	72(DE)
NOCl	116	Cl—NO	1.95	37(DE)
NOBr	117	Br—NO	2.14	28(DE)
SO_2	120	S—O	1.43	119(BE)
$SeCl_2$		Se—Cl		58(BE)
O_3	117	O—O	1.278	
NO_2^-	115	N—O	1.24	

[a]Data from T. L. Cottrell, *The Strengths of Chemical Bonds*, Butterworths, London, 1958, Table 11.5.1; L. E. Sutton (ed.), "Interatomic Distances," *Special Publication No. 11*, The Chemical Society, London, 1958.

scheme predicts $1\frac{1}{2}$ π bonds for NO, and only $\frac{1}{2}$ for the NO in NO_2; thus a longer NO bond in NO_2 is expected. The O—NO bond-dissociation energy is 72 kcal/mole.

Bond properties for a number of angular triatomic molecules are given in Table 7–2.

SUPPLEMENTARY PROBLEMS

1. Describe the electronic structures of the following molecules: (a) O_3; (b) ClO_2; (c) ClO_2^+; (d) OF_2.

2. What structure would you expect for the amide ion? for SCl_2? XeF_2?

VIII

Bonding in Organic Molecules

8–1 INTRODUCTION

Carbon atoms have a remarkable ability to form bonds with hydrogen atoms and other carbon atoms. Since carbon has one $2s$ and three $2p$ valence orbitals, the structure around carbon for *full* σ bonding is tetrahedral (sp^3). We discussed the bonding in CH_4, a simple tetrahedral molecule, in Chapter V. By replacing one hydrogen in CH_4 with a —CH_3 group, the C_2H_6 (ethane) molecule is obtained. The C_2H_6 molecule contains one C—C bond, and the structure around each carbon is tetrahedral (sp^3), as shown in Fig. 8–1. By continually replacing hydrogens with —CH_3 groups, the many *hydrocarbons* with the full sp^3 σ-bonding structure at each carbon are obtained.

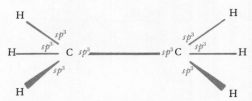

Figure 8–1   Valence-bond structure for C_2H_6.

In many organic molecules, carbon uses only three or two of its four valence orbitals for σ bonding. This leaves one or two $2p$ orbitals for π bonding. The main purpose of this chapter is to describe bonding in some of the important atomic groupings containing carbon with π valence orbitals.

It is common practice to describe the σ bonding of carbon in organic molecules in terms of the hybrid-orbital picture summarized in Table 8–1. The π bonding will be described in terms of molecular orbitals, and the energy-level schemes will refer only to the energies of the π molecular orbitals. This is a useful way of handling the electronic energy levels, since the σ bonding orbitals are usually considerably more stable than the π bonding orbitals. Thus the chemically and spectroscopically "active" electrons reside in the π molecular orbitals.

8–2 C_2H_4

The structure of ethylene, C_2H_4, is shown in Fig. 8–2. The molecule is planar, and each carbon is bonded to two hydrogens and to the other carbon. With three groups attached to each carbon, we use a set of sp^2 hybrid orbitals for σ bonding.

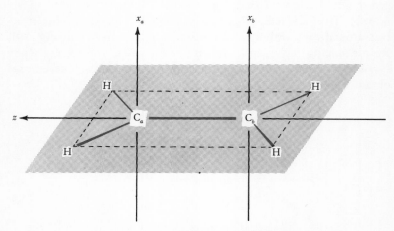

Figure 8–2   Coordinate system for C_2H_4.

Table 8-1

Hybrid-Orbital Picture for σ Bonding of Carbon in Organic Molecules

Number of atoms bound to carbon	σ Bond orbitals	Structure around carbon
4	sp^3	tetrahedral
3	sp^2	trigonal planar
2	sp	linear

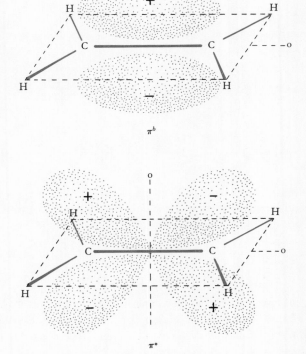

Figure 8-3 Boundary surfaces of the π molecular orbitals of C_2H_4.

This leaves each carbon with a $2p$ orbital, which is perpendicular to the plane of the molecule. We form bonding and antibonding molecular orbitals with the $2p_x$ valence orbitals, as follows:

$$\psi(\pi^b) = \frac{1}{\sqrt{2}}(x_a + x_b) \qquad (8\text{--}1)$$

$$\psi(\pi^*) = \frac{1}{\sqrt{2}}(x_a - x_b) \qquad (8\text{--}2)$$

The boundary surfaces of the π^b and π^* MO's are shown in Fig. 8–3.

8–3   ENERGY LEVELS IN C_2H_4

The energies of the π^b and π^* MO's are obtained just as were the energies of the σ^b and σ^* MO's of H_2 (Section 2–4):

$$E[\psi(\pi^b)] = \int \psi(\pi^b)\mathcal{JC}\psi(\pi^b)\,d\tau = \tfrac{1}{2}\int(x_a + x_b)\mathcal{JC}(x_a + x_b)\,d\tau$$

$$= q_c + \beta_{cc} \qquad (8\text{--}3)$$

$$E[\psi(\pi^*)] = \tfrac{1}{2}\int(x_a - x_b)\mathcal{JC}(x_a - x_b)\,d\tau = q_c - \beta_{cc} \qquad (8\text{--}4)$$

Thus we have the same type of energy-level scheme for the π molecular orbitals of ethylene as we had for the σ molecular orbitals of the hydrogen molecule. The diagram for C_2H_4 is shown in Fig. 8–4.

8–4   GROUND STATE OF C_2H_4

There are twelve valence electrons in C_2H_4, eight from the two carbons $(2s^2 2p^2)$ and one from each hydrogen. Ten of these electrons are used in σ bonding, as shown in Fig. 8–5. Two electrons are left to place in the π molecular orbitals. The ground state is $(\pi^b)^2$, which gives one π bond. The usual pictures of the bonding in C_2H_4 are shown in Fig. 8–6.

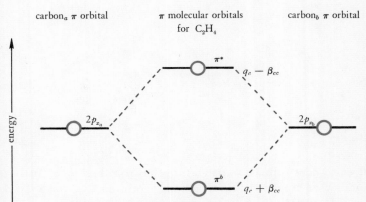

Figure 8–4 Relative π orbital energies in C_2H_4.

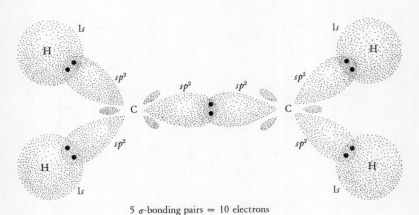

5 σ-bonding pairs = 10 electrons

Figure 8–5 The σ bonding structure of C_2H_4.

8–5 BENT-BOND PICTURE OF C_2H_4

The C=C bond can be formulated as involving two equivalent "bent" bonds, rather than one σ and one π bond. One simple way to construct equivalent bent bonds is to linearly combine the σ^b and π^b molecular orbitals of C_2H_4 as follows:

$$\psi_1 = \frac{1}{\sqrt{2}}[\psi(\sigma_{cc}{}^b) + \psi(\pi_{cc}{}^b)] \qquad (8\text{–}5)$$

$$\psi_2 = \frac{1}{\sqrt{2}}[\psi(\sigma_{cc}{}^b) - \psi(\pi_{cc}{}^b)] \qquad (8\text{–}6)$$

The equivalent orbitals ψ_1 and ψ_2 are shown in Fig. 8–7. If the σ^b orbitals used are derived from carbon sp^2 orbitals (Section 8–2), the H—C—H and H—C—C bond angles should be 120°.

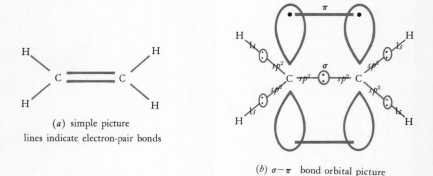

(a) simple picture
lines indicate electron-pair bonds

(b) $\sigma - \pi$ bond orbital picture

Figure 8–6 Common representations of the bonding in C_2H_4.

Using only valence-bond ideas, we can formulate the bonding in C_2H_4 as involving four sp^3 orbitals on each carbon. Two of the sp^3 orbitals are used to attach two hydrogens, and two are used to bond to the other carbon in the double bond. Thus, C_2H_4 would be represented as shown in Fig. 8–8. This model predicts an H—C—H angle of 109°28′ and an H—C=C angle of 125°16′.

The observed H—C—H angle in C_2H_4 is 117°. Since the molecule is planar, the H—C=C angle is 121.5°. These angles are much closer in size to the 120° angle between equivalent sp^2 hybrid orbitals than they are to the tetrahedral hybrid-orbital predictions. However, certain other molecules containing the C=C group have X—C=C

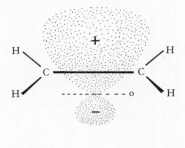

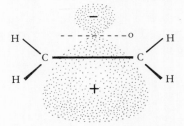

Figure 8–7 **Equivalent orbitals in C_2H_4, constructed from the σ^b and π^b orbitals.**

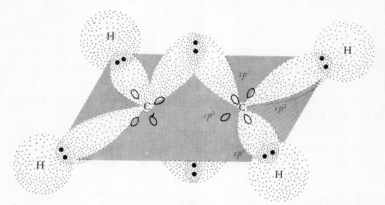

Figure 8–8   Equivalent orbitals in C_2H_4, using sp^3 orbitals on each carbon.

angles in the neighborhood of 125°.

The multiple bonds in molecules such as N_2, H_2CO, and C_2H_2 can be formulated either as equivalent bent bonds or as a combination of σ and π bonds.   For a more complete discussion of equivalent orbitals, the reader is referred elsewhere.[1]

8–6   BOND PROPERTIES OF THE C═C GROUP

There are two kinds of bonds in C_2H_4, C═C and C—H.   Thus we must know the value of BE(C—H) in order to obtain the value of BE(C═C) from the process

$$
\begin{array}{c}
H \qquad H \\
\diagdown \quad \diagup \qquad E \\
C{=}C \quad \longrightarrow C + C + H + H + H + H \qquad (8\text{–}7)\\
\diagup \quad \diagdown \\
H \qquad H
\end{array}
$$

[1] J. A. Pople, *Quart. Rev.*, **XI**, 273 (1957); L. Pauling, *Nature of the Chemical Bond*, Cornell University Press, Ithaca, N.Y., 1960, p. 138 ff.

The value of BE(C—H) used to calculate bond energies such as C=C, C=O, etc., is 98.7 kcal/mole, which is very nearly the BE(C—H) in CH$_4$. Bond energies and bond lengths for a number of important groups are given in Table 8-2. The values are averaged from several compounds unless otherwise indicated.

The average C=C bond energy is 145.8 kcal/mole, a value almost twice as large as the C—C bond energy of 82.6 kcal/mole. The C=C bond length is 1.35 A, which is shorter than the 1.54 = A C—C bond distance.

Table 8-2

Bond Properties of Organic Groups[a]

Bond	Bond length, A	Bond energy, kcal/mole
C—H	1.08	98.7
C—C	1.54	82.6
C=C	1.35	145.8
C≡C	1.21	199.6
C—C (in C$_2$H$_6$)	1.543	83(DE)
C=C (in C$_2$H$_4$)	1.353	125(DE); 142.9(BE)
C≡C (in C$_2$H$_2$)	1.207	230(DE); 194.3(BE)
C—N	1.47	72.8
C=N		147
C≡N	1.14	212.6
C—O	1.43	85.5
C=O (in aldehydes)	1.22	176
C=O (in ketones)	1.22	179
C=O (in H$_2$CO)	1.21	166
C—F (in CF$_4$)	1.36	116
C—Si [in Si(CH$_3$)$_4$]	1.93	72
C—S (in C$_2$H$_5$SH)	1.81	65
C=S (in CS$_2$)	1.55	128
C—Cl	1.76	81
C—Br	1.94 (in CH$_3$Br)	68 (in C$_2$H$_5$Br)
C—I (in CH$_3$I)	2.14	51

[a] Data from T. L. Cottrell, *The Strengths of Chemical Bonds*, Butterworths, London, 1958, Table 11.5.1.

8-7 THE VALUE OF β_{cc} IN C_2H_4

The first excited state of C_2H_4 occurs upon excitation of an electron from π^b to π^*, giving the configuration $(\pi^b)(\pi^*)$. We see that the difference in energy between π^b and π^* is -2β. Absorption of light at the 1650 A wavelength causes the $\pi^b \rightarrow \pi^*$ excitation to take place. Since 1650 A is equal to 60,600 cm^{-1} or 174 kcal/mole, we have

$$-2\beta_{cc} = 60,600 \text{ cm}^{-1} \quad \text{or} \quad 174 \text{ kcal/mole}$$

and

$$\beta_{cc} = -30,300 \text{ cm}^{-1} \quad \text{or} \quad -87 \text{ kcal/mole} \quad (8\text{-}8)$$

8-8 H_2CO

The simplest molecule containing the C=O group is formaldehyde, H_2CO. The σ bonding in H_2CO can be represented as involving sp^2 orbitals on carbon. This leaves one $2p$ orbital on carbon for π bond-

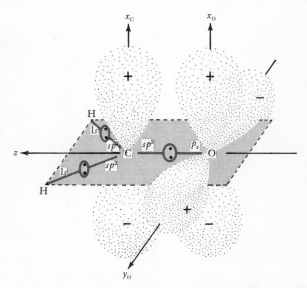

Figure 8-9   Orbitals in the H_2CO molecule.

ing to the oxygen, as shown in Fig. 8-9. The π molecular orbitals are:

$$\psi(\pi_x{}^b) = C_1 x_C + C_2 x_O \tag{8-9}$$

$$\psi(\pi_x{}^*) = C_3 x_C - C_4 x_O \tag{8-10}$$

Since oxygen is more electronegative than carbon, we expect $(C_2)^2 > (C_1)^2$ and $(C_3)^2 > (C_4)^2$. Since the oxygen $2p_z$ orbital is used in σ bonding, we have the $2p_y$ orbital remaining as a nonbonding MO of the π type. The energy-level scheme expected for the π molecular orbitals of H_2CO is shown in Fig. 8-10.

8-9   GROUND STATE OF H_2CO

There are twelve valence electrons in H_2CO, two from the hydrogens, four from carbon, and six from oxygen $(2s^2 2p^4)$. Six of these electrons are involved in σ bonding, and two are in the oxygen $2s$ orbital as a lone pair. This leaves four electrons for the π orbitals shown in Fig. 8-10. The ground state is $(\pi_x{}^b)^2(\pi_y)^2$. There is one

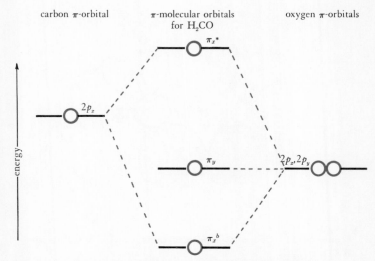

Figure 8-10   Relative π orbital energies in H_2CO.

carbon-oxygen π bond, along with the σ bond, giving an electronic structure that is commonly represented as shown in Fig. 8–11.

The carbonyl (C=O) group is present in many classes of organic compounds, among them aldehydes, ketones, esters, acids, and amides. The simplest ketone is acetone, $(CH_3)_2C=O$. The C=O bond energy in H_2CO is 166 kcal/mole. As C—H bonds are replaced by C—C bonds, the C=O bond energy increases. The average C=O bond energy for aldehydes is 176 kcal/mole; for ketones it is 179 kcal/mole. Each of these average values is more than twice the 85.5 kcal/mole value for the C—O bond energy. The average C=O bond length is 1.22 A, which lies between C≡O ($R = 1.13$ A) and C—O ($R = 1.43$ A).

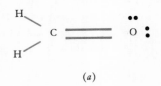

(a)

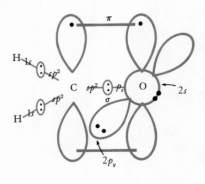

(b)

Figure 8–11 Common representations of the bonding in H_2CO.

8–10 THE $n \to \pi^*$ TRANSITION EXHIBITED BY THE CARBONYL GROUP

The excitation of an electron from π_y to π_x^* occurs with absorption of light in the 2700–3000 A wavelength region. Thus the carbonyl group exhibits a very characteristic absorption spectrum. Since the transition is from a nonbonding π orbital to an antibonding π orbital, it is commonly called an $n \to \pi^*$ transition.

8–11 C_2H_2

The structure of acetylene, C_2H_2, is shown in Fig. 8–12. The σ bonding involves sp hybrid orbitals on the carbons, leaving each carbon with two mutually perpendicular $2p$ orbitals for π bonding. The π molecular orbitals are the same as those for a homonuclear diatomic molecule:

$$\psi(\pi_x{}^b) = \frac{1}{\sqrt{2}}(x_a + x_b) \qquad (8\text{–}11)$$

$$\psi(\pi_y{}^b) = \frac{1}{\sqrt{2}}(y_a + y_b) \qquad (8\text{–}12)$$

$$\psi(\pi_x{}^*) = \frac{1}{\sqrt{2}}(x_a - x_b) \qquad (8\text{–}13)$$

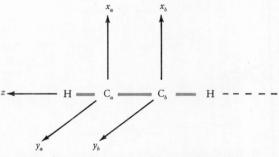

Figure 8–12   Coordinate system for C_2H_2.

$$\psi(\pi_y^*) = \frac{1}{\sqrt{2}}(y_a - y_b) \tag{8-14}$$

The energies of the π molecular orbitals are shown in Fig. 8–13.

8–12   GROUND STATE OF C_2H_2

There are ten valence electrons in C_2H_2. Six are required for σ bonding, and the other four give a ground state $(\pi_x^b)^2(\pi_y^b)^2$. Thus we have three carbon-carbon bonds, one σ bond, and two π bonds. The common bonding pictures for C_2H_2 are shown in Fig. 8–14.

The bond energy of the C≡C group, 199.6 kcal/mole, is larger than that of C—C or C=C, but smaller than that of C≡O. The C≡C bond length is 1.21 A, shorter than either C=C or C—C.

8–13 CH_3CN

The nitrile group, C≡N, is another important functional group in organic chemistry. The simple compound CH_3CN is called acetonitrile; its structure is shown in Fig. 8–15. The π bonding in the C≡N group is very similar to the π bonding in C≡C. The usual bonding pictures are also shown in Fig. 8–15.

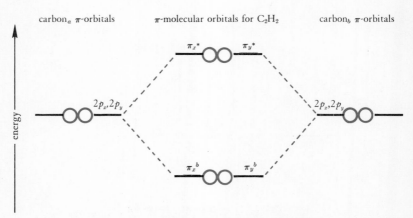

Figure 8–13   Relative orbital energies in C_2H_2.

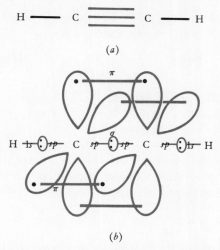

Figure 8-14   Common representations of the bonding in C_2H_2.

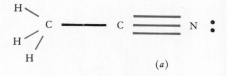

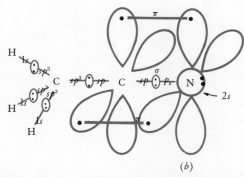

Figure 8-15   Common representations of the bonding in CH_3CN.

The C≡N bond energy, 212.6 kcal/mole, is larger than that of C≡C. The C≡N bond length is about 1.14 A.

8–14 C_6H_6

The planar structure of benzene (C_6H_6) is shown in Fig. 8–16. Each carbon is bonded to two other carbons and to one hydrogen. Thus we use sp^2 hybrid orbitals on the carbons for σ bonding. Each carbon has a $2p$ orbital for π bonding, also shown in Fig. 8–16. With six π valence orbitals, we need to construct six π molecular orbitals for C_6H_6. The most stable bonding orbital concentrates electronic density between each pair of nuclei:

$$\psi(\pi_1{}^b) = \frac{1}{\sqrt{6}}(z_a + z_b + z_c + z_d + z_e + z_f) \qquad (8\text{–}15)$$

The least stable antibonding orbital has nodes between the nuclei:

$$\psi(\pi_3{}^*) = \frac{1}{\sqrt{6}}(z_a - z_b + z_c - z_d + z_e - z_f) \qquad (8\text{–}16)$$

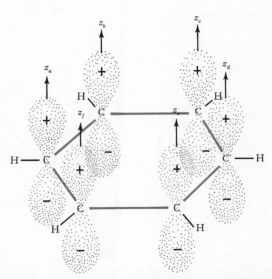

Figure 8–16   Structure and the π valence orbitals of C_6H_6.

The other molecular orbitals[1] have energies between π^b and π^*:

$$\psi(\pi_2{}^b) = \frac{1}{2\sqrt{3}}(2z_a + z_b - z_c - 2z_d - z_e + z_f) \qquad (8\text{-}17)$$

$$\psi(\pi_3{}^b) = \frac{1}{2}(z_a + z_b - z_d - z_e) \qquad (8\text{-}18)$$

$$\psi(\pi_1{}^*) = \frac{1}{2\sqrt{3}}(2z_a - z_b - z_c + 2z_d - z_e - z_f) \qquad (8\text{-}19)$$

$$\psi(\pi_2{}^*) = \frac{1}{2}(z_a - z_b + z_d - z_e) \qquad (8\text{-}20)$$

The molecular orbitals for benzene are shown in Fig. 8-17.

8-15 MOLECULAR-ORBITAL ENERGIES IN C_6H_6

The most stable orbital in benzene is $\psi(\pi_1{}^b)$. The energy of this MO is calculated below:

$$
\begin{aligned}
E[\psi(\pi_1{}^b)] &= \int \psi(\pi_1{}^b)\mathcal{H}\psi(\pi_1{}^b)\,d\tau \\
&= \tfrac{1}{6}\int (z_a + z_b + z_c + z_d + z_e + z_f)\mathcal{H} \\
&\qquad \times (z_a + z_b + z_c + z_d + z_e + z_f)\,d\tau \\
&= \tfrac{1}{6}[6q_c + 12\beta_{cc} + 2\int z_a\mathcal{H}z_c\,d\tau + 2\int z_a\mathcal{H}z_d\,d\tau + 2\int z_a\mathcal{H}z_e \\
&\qquad \times d\tau + 2\int z_b\mathcal{H}z_d\,d\tau + 2\int z_b\mathcal{H}z_e\,d\tau + 2\int z_b\mathcal{H}z_f\,d\tau \\
&\qquad + 2\int z_c\mathcal{H}z_e\,d\tau + 2\int z_c\mathcal{H}z_f\,d\tau + 2\int z_d\mathcal{H}z_f\,d\tau]
\end{aligned} \qquad (8\text{-}21)
$$

In other words, on expansion of the integral, we obtain six coulomb integrals (such as $\int z_a\mathcal{H}z_a\,d\tau$) and twelve exchange integrals involving adjacent p orbitals (such as $\int z_a\mathcal{H}z_b\,d\tau$); the other integrals are exchange integrals involving nonadjacent p orbitals (such as $\int z_a\mathcal{H}z_c\,d\tau$). We expect these integrals to be much smaller than the regular β's. If we adopt the frequently used Hückel approximation in which such integrals are taken to be zero, we have

$$E[\psi(\pi_1{}^b)] = q_c + 2\beta_{cc} \qquad (8\text{-}22)$$

The energy-level scheme for C_6H_6 is shown in Fig. 8-18.

---

[1] The rules for constructing the benzene molecular orbitals are straightforward, but require symmetry and orthogonality principles that have not been presented in this book.

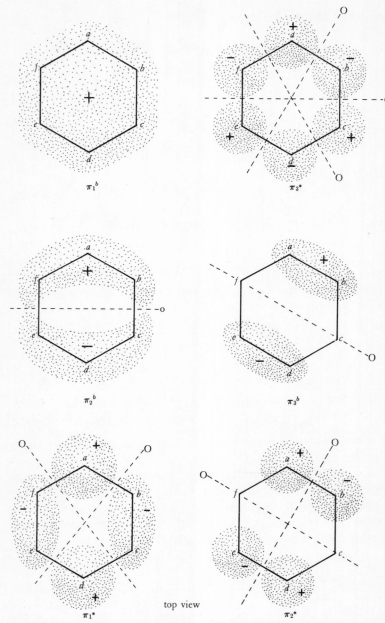

top view

Figure 8-17 Top view of the boundary surfaces of the C₆H₆ molecular orbitals.

π-molecular orbital energies in C_6H_6

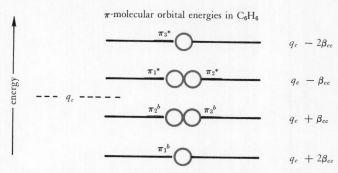

Figure 8–18   Relative energies of the π MO's in C_6H_6.

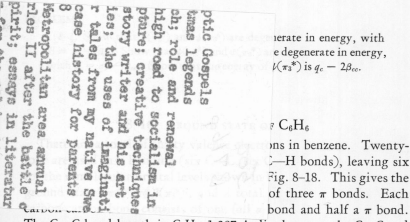

...nerate in energy, with ... degenerate in energy, ...$\nu(\pi_3^*)$ is $q_c - 2\beta_{cc}$.

... C_6H_6

...ns in benzene. Twenty-
...C—H bonds), leaving six
...Fig. 8–18. This gives the
...of three π bonds. Each
...bond and half a π bond.
The C═C bond length in C_6H_6, 1.397 A, lies between the C—C and C═C bond lengths.

The common bonding pictures of benzene are shown in Fig. 8–19.

8–17   RESONANCE ENERGY IN C_6H_6

Benzene is actually more stable than might be expected for a system of six C—C single bonds and three C—C π bonds. This added stability is due to the fact that the electrons in the three π bonds are *delocalized* over all six carbons. This is evident both from the molec-

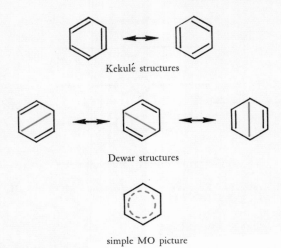

Kekulé structures

Dewar structures

simple MO picture

Figure 8–19   Common representations of the bonding in C₆H₆.

ular orbitals shown in Fig. 8–17 and from the valence-bond structures shown in Fig. 8–19.

In the MO view, the total gain in C_6H_6 stability due to π bonding is calculated in units of β_{cc} as follows:

$$2 \text{ electrons (in } \pi_1^b) \times 2\beta_{cc} = 4\beta_{cc}$$
$$2 \text{ electrons (in } \pi_2^b) \times \beta_{cc} = 2\beta_{cc}$$
$$2 \text{ electrons (in } \pi_3^b) \times \beta_{cc} = 2\beta_{cc}$$
$$\text{total} \qquad \overline{8\beta_{cc}}$$

If we did not allow the delocalization of electrons in C_6H_6, we would have a system of three *isolated* double bonds (only one of the Kekulé structures shown in Fig. 8–19). Let us calculate the π bonding stability of three isolated double bonds.

An electron in the π^b orbital of $C{=}C$ is more stable than an electron in a carbon $2p$ atomic orbital by one β_{cc} unit (see Section 8–3). With six electrons in *isolated* π^b orbitals, we have $6 \times \beta_{cc} = 6\beta_{cc}$. The *delocalization* of three π bonds in C_6H_6 gives an added stability of $8\beta_{cc} - 6\beta_{cc} = 2\beta_{cc}$. This is the calculated resonance energy in benzene.

The so-called experimental resonance energy of benzene is obtained by totaling the bond energies of the C—C, C=C, and C—H bonds present and comparing the total with the experimentally known value for the heat of formation of C_6H_6. The difference indicates that benzene is about 40 kcal/mole more stable than the sum of the bond energies for a system of six C—H, three C—C, and three isolated C=C units would suggest.

The value of β_{cc} derived from the experimental resonance energy is therefore -20 kcal/mole. This value differs substantially from the value of -87 kcal/mole obtained from the absorption spectrum of C_2H_4. It is a general result that the resonance-energy β's are much smaller than the spectroscopic β's.

SUPPLEMENTARY PROBLEMS

1. Calculate the energies of the π molecular orbitals for C_2H_2.
2. Give the "bent-bond" descriptions of C_2H_2; of H_2CO; of HCN.

IX

Bonds Involving *d*
Valence Orbitals

9–1 INTRODUCTION

There are many structures in which the central atom requires one or more *d* valence orbitals to complete a set of σ bonding orbitals. The most important of these structures are square planar, trigonal bipyramidal, square pyramidal, and octahedral; examples are shown in Fig. 9–1. Transition-metal ions have available a very stable set of *d* valence orbitals. The bonding in complexes formed between transition-metal ions and a large number of molecules and other ions undoubtedly involves *d* orbitals. In this chapter we shall describe the bonding between metal ions and ligands[1] in certain representative metal complexes.

9–2 THE OCTAHEDRAL COMPLEX $Ti(H_2O)_6^{3+}$

The Ti^{3+} ion forms a stable complex ion with six water molecules. The structure around the Ti^{3+} ion is octahedral, as shown in Fig. 9–2.

---

[1] Groups attached to metal ions in complexes are called ligands.

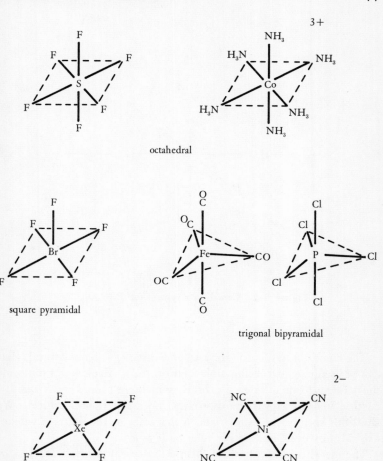

octahedral

square pyramidal

trigonal bipyramidal

square planar

Figure 9-1 Examples of structures in which *d* orbitals are used in bonding.

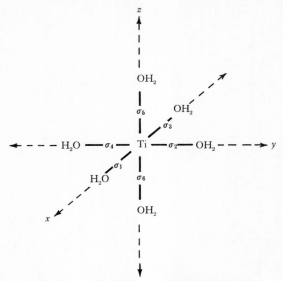

Figure 9-2 Coordinate system for $Ti(H_2O)_6{}^{3+}$.

The titanium has five $3d$, one $4s$, and three $4p$ valence orbitals that can be used in constructing molecular orbitals. Each water molecule must furnish one σ valence orbital, which, in accord with the discussion in Chapter VIII, is approximately an sp^3 hybrid orbital. We shall not specify the exact s and p character of the water σ valence orbital, however, but simply refer to it as σ.

The metal orbitals that can form σ molecular orbitals are $3d_{x^2-y^2}$, $3d_{z^2}$, $4s$, $4p_x$, $4p_y$, and $4p_z$. Since the sign of the $4s$ orbital does not change over the boundary surface, the proper linear combination of ligand orbitals for $4s$ is

$$\sigma_1 + \sigma_2 + \sigma_3 + \sigma_4 + \sigma_5 + \sigma_6 \qquad (9\text{-}1)$$

This is shown in Fig. 9-3. The wave function for the molecular orbital involving the metal $4s$ orbital is therefore

$$\psi(\sigma_s) = c_1 4s + c_2(\sigma_1 + \sigma_2 + \sigma_3 + \sigma_4 + \sigma_5 + \sigma_6) \qquad (9\text{-}2)$$

We find the other molecular orbitals by matching the metal-orbital

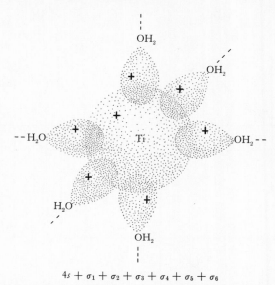

$$4s + \sigma_1 + \sigma_2 + \sigma_3 + \sigma_4 + \sigma_5 + \sigma_6$$

Figure 9-3 Overlap of the titanium 4s orbital with the σ orbitals of the water molecules.

lobes with ligand σ orbitals that have the proper sign and magnitude. This procedure is shown in Fig. 9–4. The wave functions are:

$$\psi(\sigma_x) = c_3 4p_x \quad + c_4(\sigma_1 - \sigma_3) \tag{9-3}$$

$$\psi(\sigma_y) = c_3 4p_y \quad + c_4(\sigma_2 - \sigma_4) \tag{9-4}$$

$$\psi(\sigma_z) = c_3 4p_z \quad + c_4(\sigma_5 - \sigma_6) \tag{9-5}$$

$$\psi(\sigma_{x^2-y^2}) = c_5 3d_{x^2-y^2} + c_6(\sigma_1 - \sigma_2 + \sigma_3 - \sigma_4) \tag{9-6}$$

$$\psi(\sigma_{z^2}) = c_7 3d_{z^2} \quad + c_8(2\sigma_5 + 2\sigma_6 - \sigma_1 - \sigma_2 - \sigma_3 - \sigma_4) \tag{9-7}$$

9–3 ENERGY LEVELS IN $Ti(H_2O)_6^{3+}$

Figure 9–4 shows $4p_x$, $4p_y$, and $4p_z$ to be equivalent in an octahedral complex; on this basis the σ_x, σ_y, and σ_z molecular orbitals are degenerate in energy. Although it is not obvious from Fig. 9–4, the

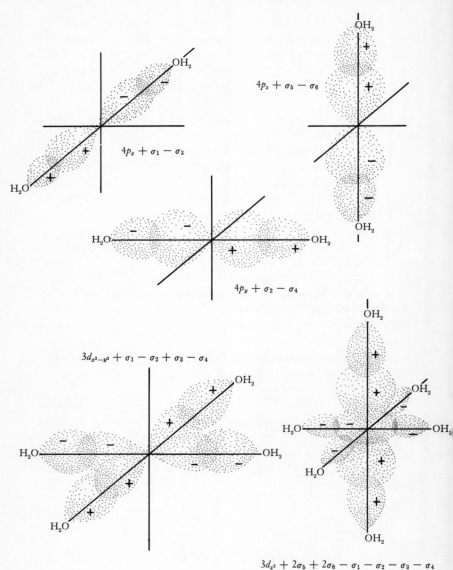

Figure 9-4 Overlap of the titanium $3d$ and $4p$ σ orbitals with the σ orbitals of the water molecules.

$3d_{x^2-y^2}$ and $3d_{z^2}$ orbitals are also equivalent in an octahedral complex, and $\sigma_{x^2-y^2}$ and σ_{z^2} are degenerate in energy. We shall solve a problem at the end of this chapter to prove the equivalence of $3d_{x^2-y^2}$ and $3d_{z^2}$. Finally, we see that, including the σ_s orbital, there are three sets of σ molecular orbitals in an octahedral complex: σ_s; σ_x, σ_y, σ_z; and $\sigma_{x^2-y^2}$, σ_{z^2}.

We have used all but three of the metal valence orbitals in the σ molecular orbitals. We are left with $3d_{xz}$, $3d_{yz}$, and $3d_{xy}$. These orbitals are situated properly for π bonding in an octahedral complex, as will be discussed later. However, since water is not a good π bonding ligand, we shall consider that the $3d_{xz}$, $3d_{yz}$, and $3d_{xy}$ orbitals are essentially nonbonding in $Ti(H_2O)_6^{3+}$. The three d_π orbitals are clearly equivalent in an octahedral complex, and we have the degenerate set: π_{xz}, π_{yz}, π_{xy}.

In order to construct an energy-level diagram for $Ti(H_2O)_6^{3+}$, we must know something about the relative energies of the starting orbitals $3d$, $4s$, $4p$, and σ_{H_2O}. In this case, σ_{H_2O} is more stable than any of the metal valence orbitals. This is fairly general in metal complexes, and in energy-level diagrams the ligand σ valence orbitals are shown to be more stable than the corresponding metal valence orbitals. It is also generally true that the order of increasing energy for the metal valence orbitals in transition-metal complexes is $nd < (n+1)s < (n+1)p$.

The energy-level diagram for $Ti(H_2O)_6^{3+}$ is shown in Fig. 9-5. There are three sets of bonding orbitals and three sets of antibonding orbitals. The virtually nonbonding $\pi(d)$ orbitals are less stable than the bonding $\sigma(d)$ set but more stable than the antibonding $\sigma(d)$ set. The relative energies of the three bonding σ sets are not known. The order given in Fig. 9-5 was obtained from a calculation that is beyond the level of our discussion.

9-4 GROUND STATE OF $Ti(H_2O)_6^{3+}$

We must count every electron in the valence orbitals used to construct the diagram in Fig. 9-5. The complex is considered to be composed of Ti^{3+} and six water molecules. Each of the six σ valence orbitals of the water molecules furnishes two electrons, for a total of

Ti orbitals   Ti(H$_2$O)$_6^{3+}$ orbitals   H$_2$O orbitals

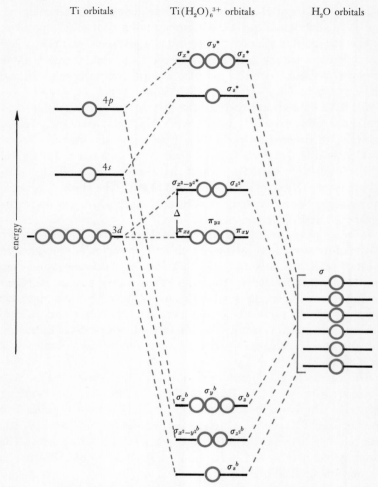

Figure 9–5   Relative orbital energies in Ti(H$_2$O)$_6^{3+}$.

twelve.   Since the electronic structure of Ti^{3+} is $(3d)^1$, we have a
total of thirteen electrons to place in the molecular orbitals shown
in Fig. 9–5.   The ground state of Ti(H$_2$O)$_6^{3+}$ is therefore

$$(\sigma_s{}^b)^2(\sigma^b_{x,y,z})^6(\sigma^b_{x^2-y^2,z^2})^4(\pi_{xz,yz,xy})^1 \qquad S = \tfrac{1}{2}$$

There is one unpaired electron in the $\pi(d)$ level. Consistent with this ground state, $Ti(H_2O)_6^{3+}$ is paramagnetic, with $S = \frac{1}{2}$.

The electrons in σ bonding orbitals are mainly localized on the water molecules, since the σ valence orbital of H_2O is more stable than the metal orbitals. The nonbonding and antibonding orbitals, on the other hand, are mainly located on the metal. We shall focus our attention in the sections to follow on the molecular orbitals that are mainly based on the metal and derived from the $3d$ valence orbitals.

9–5   THE ELECTRONIC SPECTRUM OF $Ti(H_2O)_6^{3+}$

The difference in energy between $\sigma^*(d)$ and $\pi(d)$ is called Δ or $10Dq$. Excitation of the electron in $\pi(d)$ to $\sigma^*(d)$ occurs with absorption of light in the visible region of the spectrum, and $Ti(H_2O)_6^{3+}$ is therefore colored reddish-violet. The electronic spectrum of $Ti(H_2O)_6^{3+}$ is shown in Fig. 9–6. The maximum absorption occurs at 4930 A, or 20,300 cm^{-1}. The value of the splitting Δ is usually expressed in cm^{-1} units; thus we say that $Ti(H_2O)_6^{3+}$ has a Δ of 20,300 cm^{-1}.

The colors of many other transition-metal complexes are also due to such "d–d" transitions.

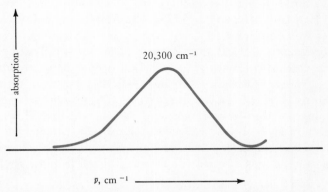

Figure 9–6   The absorption spectrum of $Ti(H_2O)_6^{3+}$ in the visible region.

9–6   VALENCE-BOND THEORY FOR $Ti(H_2O)_6^{3+}$

The localized bonding scheme for $Ti(H_2O)_6^{3+}$ is obtained by first constructing six equivalent hybrid orbitals that are octahedrally directed. We use the six σ valence orbitals of Ti for this purpose: $3d_{x^2-y^2}$, $3d_{z^2}$, $4s$, $4p_x$, $4p_y$, and $4p_z$. Thus we want to construct six d^2sp^3 hybrid orbitals, each with one-third d character, one-sixth s character, and one-half p character.

Referring back to Fig. 9–2, let us form linear combinations of the d, s, and p valence orbitals that direct large lobes at the six ligands. We first construct the orbitals that are directed toward ligands ⑤ and ⑥. We shall call these orbitals ψ_5 and ψ_6, respectively. The metal orbitals that can σ bond with ⑤ and ⑥ are $3d_{z^2}$, $4s$, and $4p_z$. Choosing the coefficients of the $3d_{z^2}$, $4s$, and $4p_z$ orbitals so that ψ_5 and ψ_6 have the desired d, s, and p character, we obtain the following hybrid-orbital wave functions:

$$\psi_5 = \frac{1}{\sqrt{3}}\, 3d_{z^2} + \frac{1}{\sqrt{6}}\, 4s + \frac{1}{\sqrt{2}}\, 4p_z \qquad (9\text{–}8)$$

$$\psi_6 = \frac{1}{\sqrt{3}}\, 3d_{z^2} + \frac{1}{\sqrt{6}}\, 4s - \frac{1}{\sqrt{2}}\, 4p_z \qquad (9\text{–}9)$$

The positive coefficient of $4p_z$ in ψ_5 directs a large lobe toward ⑤, and the negative coefficient of $4p_z$ in ψ_6 directs a large lobe toward ⑥.

The orbitals directed toward ① and ③ are constructed from the $3d_{x^2-y^2}$, $3d_{z^2}$, $4s$ and $4p_x$ metal orbitals. The orbitals directed toward ② and ④ are constructed from the $3d_{x^2-y^2}$, $3d_{z^2}$, $4s$, and $4p_y$ orbitals. The coefficients of $4s$ and $4p$ pose no problem, but we have to divide the one-third d character in each hybrid orbital between $3d_{z^2}$ and $3d_{x^2-y^2}$. We see from Eqs. (9–8) and (9–9) that we have "used up" two-thirds of the $3d_{z^2}$ orbital in ψ_5 and ψ_6. Thus we must divide the remaining one-third equally among ψ_1, ψ_2, ψ_3, and ψ_4. This means that each of ψ_1, ψ_2, ψ_3, and ψ_4 has one-twelfth $3d_{z^2}$ character and one-fourth $3d_{x^2-y^2}$ character. Choosing the signs of the coefficients so that a large lobe is directed toward each ligand in turn, we have:

$$\psi_1 = \tfrac{1}{2}\, 3d_{x^2-y^2} - \frac{1}{\sqrt{12}}\, 3d_{z^2} + \frac{1}{\sqrt{6}}\, 4s + \frac{1}{\sqrt{2}}\, 4p_x \qquad (9\text{–}10)$$

$$\psi_2 = -\tfrac{1}{2}\, 3d_{x^2-y^2} - \frac{1}{\sqrt{12}}\, 3d_{z^2} + \frac{1}{\sqrt{6}}\, 4s + \frac{1}{\sqrt{2}}\, 4p_y \qquad (9\text{-}11)$$

$$\psi_3 = \quad \tfrac{1}{2}\, 3d_{x^2-y^2} - \frac{1}{\sqrt{12}}\, 3d_{z^2} + \frac{1}{\sqrt{6}}\, 4s - \frac{1}{\sqrt{2}}\, 4p_x \qquad (9\text{-}12)$$

$$\psi_4 = -\tfrac{1}{2}\, 3d_{x^2-y^2} - \frac{1}{\sqrt{12}}\, 3d_{z^2} + \frac{1}{\sqrt{6}}\, 4s - \frac{1}{\sqrt{2}}\, 4p_y \qquad (9\text{-}13)$$

These six localized d^2sp^3 orbitals are used to form electron-pair bonds with the six water molecules. The valence-bond description of the ground state of $Ti(H_2O)_6^{3+}$ is shown in Fig. 9–7. The unpaired elec-

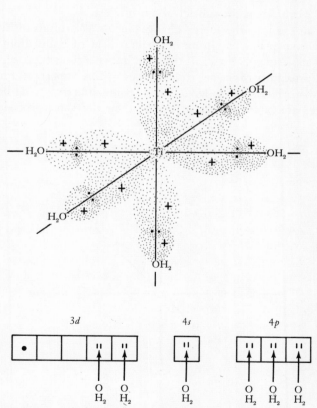

Figure 9–7 **Valence-bond representations of $Ti(H_2O)_6{}^{3+}$.**

tron is placed in one of the d orbitals that has not been used to construct hybrid bond orbitals. This simple valence-bond orbital diagram is also shown in Fig. 9–7.

9–7 CRYSTAL-FIELD THEORY FOR $Ti(H_2O)_6^{3+}$

In the crystal-field-theory formulation of a metal complex, we consider the ligands as point charges or point dipoles. The crystal-field model is shown in Fig. 9–8. The point charges or point dipoles constitute an electrostatic field, which has the symmetry of the complex. The effect of this electrostatic field on the energies of the metal d orbitals is the subject of our interest.

Let us examine the energy changes in the $3d$ orbitals of Ti^{3+} that result from placement in an octahedral field of point dipoles (the water molecules). First, all the d orbital energies are raised, owing to the proximity of the negative charges. More important, however, the two orbitals $(3d_{z^2}, 3d_{x^2-y^2})$ that point directly at the negative charges are raised higher in energy than the three orbitals $(3d_{xz},$

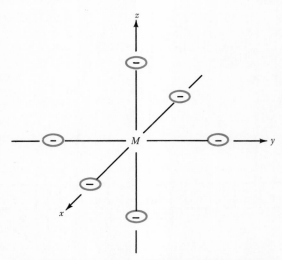

Figure 9–8   An octahedral field of point charges.

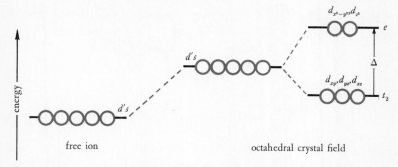

Figure 9–9   Splitting of the metal *d* **orbitals in an octahedral crystal field.**

$3d_{yz}$, $3d_{xy}$) that are directed at points between the negative charges. Thus we have a splitting of the five *d* orbitals in an octahedral crystal field as shown in Fig. 9–9.   It is convenient to use the group-theoretical symbols for the split *d* levels.   The $3d_{z^2}$ and $3d_{x^2-y^2}$ orbitals form the degenerate set called *e*, and the $3d_{xz}$, $3d_{yz}$, and $3d_{xy}$ orbitals form the degenerate set called t_2.   The separation of *e* and t_2 is again designated Δ or $10Dq$.

The one *d* electron in Ti^{3+} is placed in the more stable t_2 orbitals in the ground state.   The excitation of this electron from t_2 to *e* is responsible for the spectral band shown in Fig. 9–6.

9–8   RELATIONSHIP OF THE GENERAL MOLECULAR-ORBITAL TREATMENT TO THE VALENCE-BOND AND CRYSTAL-FIELD THEORIES

The valence-bond and crystal-field theories describe different parts of the general molecular-orbital diagram shown in Fig. 9–5.   The σ bonding molecular orbitals are related to the six d^2sp^3 bonding orbitals of the valence-bond theory.   The valence-bond theory does not include the antibonding orbitals, and therefore does not provide an explanation for the spectral bands of metal complexes.   The t_2 and *e* levels of the crystal-field theory are related to the $\pi(d)$ and $\sigma^*(d)$ molecular orbitals.   A diagram showing the relationship between the three theories is given in Fig. 9–10.

crystal-field splitting related to splitting between $\sigma^*(d)$ and $\pi(d)$ molecular orbitals

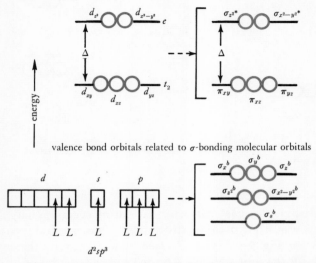

valence bond orbitals related to σ-bonding molecular orbitals

Figure 9–10 Comparison of the three theories used to describe the electronic structures of transition-metal complexes.

9–9 TYPES OF π BONDING IN METAL COMPLEXES

The d_{xz}, d_{yz}, and d_{xy} orbitals may be used for π bonding in octahedral complexes. Consider a complex containing six chloride ligands. Each of the d_π orbitals overlaps with four ligand π orbitals, as shown in Fig. 9–11. In the bonding orbital, some electronic charge from the chloride is transferred to the metal. We call this *ligand-to-metal* $(L \rightarrow M)$ π bonding. The π orbitals based on the metal are destabilized in the process and are made antibonding.

If the complex contains a diatomic ligand such as CN^-, two types of π bonding are possible. Recall from Chapter II that CN^- has filled π^b and empty π^* molecular orbitals, as shown in Fig. 9–12. The occupied π^b orbitals can enter into $L \rightarrow M$ π bonding with the $3d_{xz}$, $3d_{yz}$, and $3d_{xy}$ orbitals. In addition, however, electrons in the metal $\pi(d)$ level can be delocalized into the available π^* (CN^-) orbitals, thus preventing the accumulation of too much negative

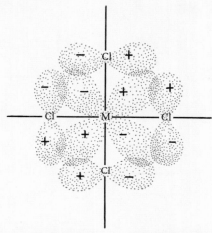

Figure 9–11 Overlap of a d_π orbital with four ligand π orbitals in an octahedral complex.

charge on the metal. This type of bonding removes electronic density from the metal and is called *metal-to-ligand* $(M \to L)$ π bonding. It is also commonly called *back donation* or *back bonding*. Back donation stabilizes the $\pi(d)$ level and makes it less antibonding. Both types of π bonding between a d_π orbital and CN^- are shown in Fig. 9–12.

9–10 SQUARE-PLANAR COMPLEXES

A simple square-planar complex is $PtCl_4^{2-}$. The coordinate system that we shall use to discuss the bonding in $PtCl_4^{2-}$ is pictured in Fig. 9–13.

The metal valence orbitals suitable for σ molecular orbitals are $5d_{x^2-y^2}$, $5d_{z^2}$, $6s$, $6p_x$, and $6p_y$. Of the two d σ valence orbitals, it is clear that $5d_{x^2-y^2}$ interacts strongly with the four ligand σ valence orbitals and that $5d_{z^2}$ interacts weakly (most of the $5d_{z^2}$ orbital is directed along the z axis).

The $5d_{xz}$, $5d_{yz}$, and $5d_{xy}$ orbitals are involved in π bonding with the ligands. The $5d_{xy}$ orbital interacts with π valence orbitals on all four

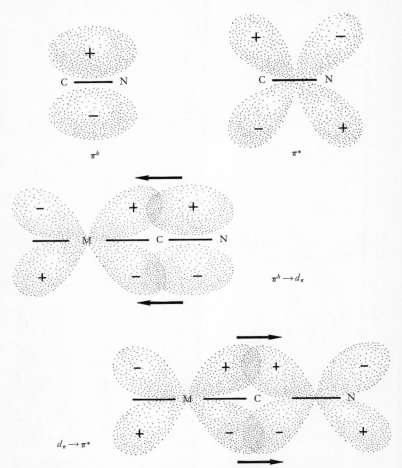

Figure 9–12   Types of π bonding between CN^- and a metal d_π orbital.

ligands, whereas $5d_{xz}$ and $5d_{yz}$ are equivalent and interact with only two ligands. The overlap of the metal $5d$ orbitals with the valence orbitals of the four ligands is shown in Fig. 9–14.

We can now construct an approximate energy-level diagram for $PtCl_4^{2-}$. We shall not attempt to pinpoint all the levels, but instead

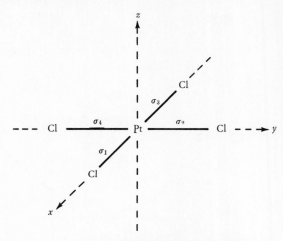

Figure 9–13   Coordinate system for PtCl$_4^{2-}$.

to recognize a few important regions of energy. A simplified energy-level diagram for PtCl$_4^{2-}$ is shown in Fig. 9–15. The most stable orbitals are σ bonding and are located on the chlorides. Next in order of stability are the π molecular orbitals, also mainly based on the four chlorides. The molecular orbitals derived from the $5d$ valence orbitals are in the middle of the diagram. They are the antibonding partners of the σ and π bonding orbitals just described.

We can confidently place the strongly antibonding $\sigma^*_{x^2-y^2}$ highest. We can also place π_{xy}^* above $\pi^*_{xz,yz}$, since $3d_{xy}$ interacts with all four ligands (see Fig. 9–14). The weakly antibonding $\sigma_{z^2}^*$ is believed to lie between π_{xy}^* and $\pi^*_{xz,yz}$. However, regardless of the placement of $\sigma_{z^2}^*$, the most important characteristic of the energy levels in a square-planar complex is that one d level has very high energy whereas the other four are much more stable and bunched together.

Since Pt^{2+} is $5d^8$ and since the four chlorides furnish eight σ and sixteen π electrons, the ground state of PtCl$_4^{2-}$ is

$$(\sigma^b)^8(\pi)^{16}(\pi^*_{xz,yz})^4(\sigma^*_{z^2})^2(\pi_{xy}^*)^2 \qquad S = 0$$

The complex is diamagnetic since the eight metal valence electrons

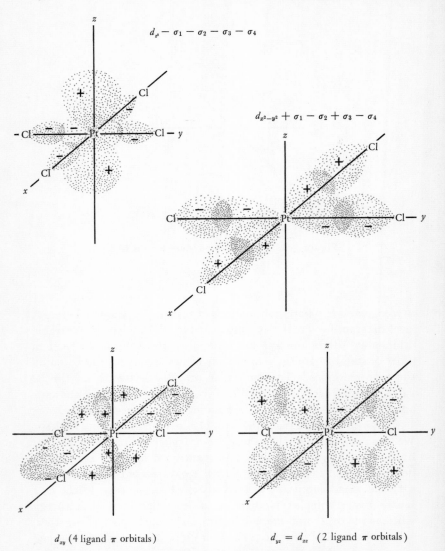

$d_{z^2} - \sigma_1 - \sigma_2 - \sigma_3 - \sigma_4$

$d_{x^2-y^2} + \sigma_1 - \sigma_2 + \sigma_3 - \sigma_4$

d_{xy} (4 ligand π orbitals) $d_{yz} = d_{xz}$ (2 ligand π orbitals)

Figure 9-14   Overlap of the metal d valence orbitals with the ligand valence orbitals in a square-planar complex.

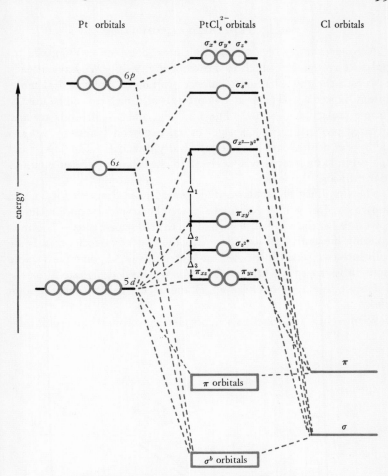

Figure 9–15   Relative orbital energies in $PtCl_4^{2-}$.

are paired in the more stable d levels.   It is easy to see from the energy-level diagram that the best electronic situation for a square-planar complex is d^8.   This observation is consistent with the fact that the d^8 metal ions, among them Ni^{2+}, Pd^{2+}, Pt^{2+}, and Au^{3+}, form a great number of square-planar complexes.

9–11   TETRAHEDRAL COMPLEXES

A good example of a tetrahedral metal complex is VCl_4, the co-ordinate system for which is shown in Fig. 9–16.   We have already discussed the role of s and p valence orbitals in a tetrahedral mole-cule (Chapter V).   The $4s$ and $4p$ orbitals of vanadium can be used to form σ molecular orbitals.   The $3d_{xz}$, $3d_{yz}$, and $3d_{xy}$ orbitals are also situated properly for such use.   In valence-bond language, sd^3 and sp^3 hybrid orbitals are both tetrahedrally directed.   The $3d_{x^2-y^2}$ and $3d_{z^2}$ orbitals interact very weakly with the ligands to form π molec-ular orbitals.

The simplified molecular-orbital energy-level diagram for VCl_4 is shown in Fig. 9–17.   Again we place the stable σ bonding levels lowest, with the π levels, localized on the chlorides, next.   The anti-bonding molecular orbitals derived from the $3d$ valence orbitals are split into two sets, those based on $3d_{xz}$, $3d_{yz}$, and $3d_{xy}$ being less stable than those based on $3d_{z^2}$ and $3d_{x^2-y^2}$.   We shall designate Δ_t as the difference in energy between $\sigma^*(d)$ and $\pi^*(d)$ in a tetrahedral com-plex.

With eight σ and sixteen π valence electrons from the four chlorides

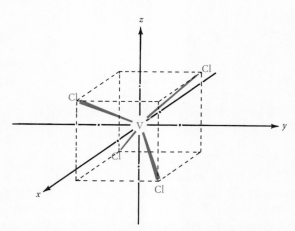

Figure 9–16   Coordinate system for VCl_4.

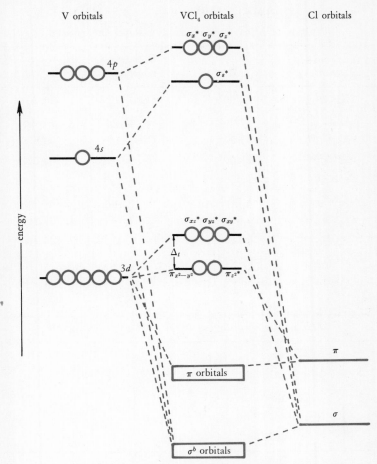

Figure 9–17   Relative orbital energies in VCl₄

and with one valence electron from V^{4+} ($3d^1$), the ground state of VCl₄ is

$$[\sigma^b]^8[\pi]^{16}[\pi^*(d)]^1 \qquad S = \tfrac{1}{2}$$

The paramagnetism of VCl₄ is consistent with the ground state, there being one unpaired electron.

Table 9-1

Values of Δ for Representative Metal Complexes

Octahedral complexes	Δ, cm^{-1}	Octahedral complexes	Δ, cm^{-1}
$Ti(H_2O)_6^{3+}$	20,300[a]	$Co(H_2O)_6^{3+}$	18,200[c]
TiF_6^{3-}	17,000[b]	$Co(NH_3)_6^{3+}$	22,900[c]
$V(H_2O)_6^{3+}$	17,850[a]	$Co(CN)_6^{3-}$	34,800[d]
$V(H_2O)_6^{2+}$	12,400[c]	$Co(H_2O)_6^{2+}$	9,300[c]
$Cr(H_2O)_6^{3+}$	17,400[c]	$Ni(H_2O)_6^{2+}$	8,500[c]
$Cr(NH_3)_6^{3+}$	21,600[c]	$Ni(NH_3)_6^{2+}$	10,800[c]
$Cr(CN)_6^{3-}$	26,600[d]	$RhCl_6^{3-}$	20,300[c]
$Cr(CO)_6$	34,150[d]	$Rh(NH_3)_6^{3+}$	34,100[c]
$Fe(CN)_6^{3-}$	35,000[d]	$RhBr_6^{3-}$	19,000[c]
$Fe(CN)_6^{4-}$	33,800[d]	$IrCl_6^{3-}$	25,000[c]
		$Ir(NH_3)_6^{3+}$	40,000[e]

Tetrahedral complexes	Δ, cm^{-1}
VCl_4	9000[a]
$CoCl_4^{2-}$	3300[f]
$CoBr_4^{2-}$	2900[f]
CoI_4^{2-}	2700[f]
$Co(NCS)_4^{2-}$	4700[f]

Square-planar complexes[g]	Δ_1, cm^{-1}	Δ_2, cm^{-1}	Δ_3, cm^{-1}	Total Δ, cm^{-1}
$PdCl_4^{2-}$	19,150	6200	1450	26,800
$PdBr_4^{2-}$	18,450	5400	1350	25,200
$PtCl_4^{2-}$	23,450	5900	4350	33,700
$PtBr_4^{2-}$	22,150	6000	3550	31,700
$Ni(CN)_4^{2-}$	24,950	9900	650	35,500

(Footnotes appear on next page)

Excitation of the electron in $\pi^*(d)$ to $\sigma^*(d)$ is accompanied by light absorption, with a maximum at 9000 cm^{-1}. Thus Δ_t for VCl$_4$ is 9000 cm^{-1}.

9-12 THE VALUE OF Δ

The splitting of the molecular orbitals derived from metal d valence orbitals involves a quantity that is of considerable interest when discussing the electronic structures of metal complexes. The Δ values for a representative selection of octahedral, square-planar, and tetrahedral complexes are given in Table 9–1. The value of Δ depends on a number of variables, the most important being the geometry of the complex, the nature of the ligand, the charge on the central metal ion, and the principal quantum number n of the d valence orbitals. We shall discuss these variables individually.

Geometry of the Complex

By extrapolating the data in Table 9–1, we may estimate that, other things being equal, the total d-orbital splitting decreases as follows:

$$\text{square planar} > \text{octahedral} > \text{tetrahedral}$$
$$1.3\Delta_0 \qquad\qquad \Delta_0 \qquad\qquad 0.45\Delta_0$$

In the molecular-orbital theory, the d-orbital splitting is interpreted as the difference between the strengths of σ and π bonding as measured by the difference in energy between the σ^* and π (or π^*) molecular orbitals. The tetrahedral splitting is smallest because the d orbitals are not involved in strong σ bonding. In both octahedral and square-planar complexes, d orbitals *are* involved in strong σ bond-

---

[a]C. J. Ballhausen, *Introduction to Ligand Field Theory*, McGraw-Hill, New York, 1962, Chap. 10.

[b]H. Bedon, S. M. Horner, and S. Y. Tyree, *Inorg. Chem.*, **3**, 647 (1964).

[c]C. K. Jørgensen, *Absorption Spectra and Chemical Bonding*, Pergamon, London, 1962, Table 11.

[d]H. B. Gray and N. A. Beach, *J. Am. Chem. Soc.*, **85**, 2922 (1963).

[e]H. B. Gray, unpublished results.

[f]Averaged from values in Ref. c and in F. A. Cotton, D. M. L. Goodgame, and M. Goodgame, *J. Am. Chem. Soc.*, **83**, 4690 (1961).

[g]H. B. Gray and C. J. Ballhausen, *J. Am. Chem. Soc.*, **85**, 260 (1963).

ing, but the total square-planar splitting $(\Delta_1 + \Delta_2 + \Delta_3)$ will always be larger than the octahedral splitting since the d_{xz} and d_{yz} orbitals interact with only two ligands in a square-planar complex (as opposed to four in an octahedral complex; see Fig. 9–11).

Nature of the Ligand: the Spectrochemical Series

The spectrochemical series represents the ordering of ligands in terms of their ability to split the $\sigma^*(d)$ and $\pi(d)$ molecular orbitals. Complexes containing ligands such as CN^- and CO, which are high in the spectrochemical series, have Δ values in the range of 30,000 cm^{-1}. At the other end of the series, Br^- and I^- cause very small splittings—in many cases less than 10,000 cm^{-1}. We have already discussed the important types of metal-ligand bonding in transition-metal complexes. The manner in which each type affects the value of Δ is illustrated in Fig. 9–18. We see that a strong ligand-to-metal σ interaction *destabilizes* $\sigma^*(d)$, *increasing* the value of Δ. A strong $L \rightarrow M$ π interaction *destabilizes* $\pi(d)$, *decreasing* the value of Δ. A strong $M \rightarrow L$ π interaction *stabilizes* $\pi(d)$, *increasing* the value of Δ. It is striking that the spectrochemical series correlates reasonably

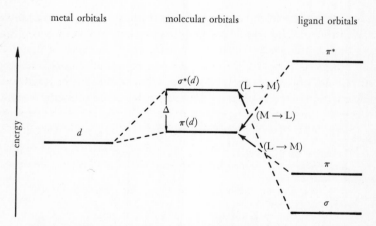

Figure 9–18   The effect of interaction of the ligand σ, π, and π^* orbitals on the value of Δ.

well with the π-bonding abilities of the ligands. The good π-*acceptor* ligands (those capable of strong $M \rightarrow L$ π bonding) cause large splittings, whereas the good π-*donor* ligands (those capable of strong $L \rightarrow M$ π bonding) cause small splittings. The ligands with intermediate Δ values have little or no π-bonding capabilities.

The spectrochemical-series order of some important ligands is indicated below:

$-CO, -CN^- > -NO_2^- > o\text{-phen}^1 > NH_3 > OH_2 > OH^-, F^-$

π acceptors $\qquad$ non-π-bonding $\quad$ weak π donors

$> SCN^-, Cl^- > Br^- > I^-$

π donors

Charge on the Central Metal Ion

In complexes containing ligands that are not good π acceptors, Δ increases with increasing positive charge on the central metal ion. A good example is the comparison between $V(H_2O)_6^{2+}$, with $\Delta = 11,800$ cm^{-1}, and $V(H_2O)_6^{3+}$, with $\Delta = 17,850$ cm^{-1}. The increase in Δ in these cases is interpreted as a substantial increase in σ bonding on increasing the positive charge of the central metal ion. This would result in an increase in the *difference* in energy between $\sigma^*(d)$ and $\pi(d)$.

In complexes containing good π-acceptor ligands, an increase in positive charge on the metal does not seem to be accompanied by a substantial increase in Δ. For example, both $Fe(CN)_6^{4-}$ and $Fe(CN)_6^{3-}$ have Δ values of approximately 34,000 cm^{-1}. In the transition from $Fe(CN)_6^{4-}$ to $Fe(CN)_6^{3-}$, the $\pi(d)$ level is destabilized just as much as the $\sigma^*(d)$ level, probably the result of a decrease in $M \rightarrow L$ π bonding when the positive charge on the metal ion is increased.

---

[1] *o*-phen is

Principal Quantum Number of the d *Valence Orbitals*

In an analogous series of complexes, the value of Δ varies with n in the d valence orbitals as follows: $3d < 4d < 5d$. For example, the Δ values for $Co(NH_3)_6{}^{3+}$, $Rh(NH_3)_6{}^{3+}$, and $Ir(NH_3)_6{}^{3+}$ are 22,900, 34,100, and 40,000 cm^{-1}, respectively. Presumably the $5d$ and $4d$ valence orbitals are better than the $3d$ in σ bonding with the ligands.

9–13   THE MAGNETIC PROPERTIES OF COMPLEXES: WEAK- AND STRONG-FIELD LIGANDS

We shall now consider in some detail the ground-state electronic configurations of octahedral complexes containing metal ions with more than one valence electron. Referring back to Fig. 9–5, we see that metal ions with one, two, and three valence electrons will have the respective ground-state configurations $\pi(d)$, $S = \frac{1}{2}$; $[\pi(d)]^2$, $S = 1$; and $[\pi(d)]^3$, $S = \frac{3}{2}$. There are two possibilities for the metal d^4 configuration, depending on the value of Δ in the complex. If Δ is less than the energy required to pair two d electrons in the $\pi(d)$ level, the fourth electron will go into the $\sigma^*(d)$ level, giving the configuration $[\pi(d)]^3[\sigma^*(d)]^1$ and four unpaired electrons $(S = 2)$. Ligands that cause such small splittings are called *weak-field* ligands.

On the other hand, if Δ is larger than the required pairing energy, the fourth electron will prefer to go into the more stable $\pi(d)$ level and pair with one of the three electrons already present in this level. The ground-state configuration of the complex in this situation is $[\pi(d)]^4$, with only two unpaired electrons $(S = 1)$. Ligands that cause splittings large enough to allow electrons to preferentially occupy the more stable $\pi(d)$ level are called *strong-field* ligands.

It is clear that, in filling the $\pi(d)$ and $\sigma^*(d)$ levels, the configurations d^4, d^5, d^6, and d^7 can have either of two possible values of S, depending on the value of Δ in the complex. When there is such a choice, the complexes with the larger S values are called *high-spin* complexes, and those with smaller S values are called *low-spin* complexes. The paramagnetism of the high-spin complexes is larger than that of the low-spin complexes. Examples of octahedral complexes with the possible $[\pi(d)]^x[\sigma^*(d)]^y$ configurations are given in Table 9–2.

Table 9-2

Electronic Configurations of Octahedral Complexes

Electronic configuration of the metal ion		Electronic structure of the complex	Example
$3d^1$		$[\pi(d)]^1$	$Ti(H_2O)_6^{3+}$
$3d^2$		$[\pi(d)]^2$	$V(H_2O)_6^{3+}$
$3d^3$		$[\pi(d)]^3$	$Cr(H_2O)_6^{3+}$
$3d^4$	low-spin	$[\pi(d)]^4$	$Mn(CN)_6^{3-}$
	high-spin	$[\pi(d)]^3[\sigma*(d)]$	$Cr(H_2O)_6^{2+}$
$3d^5$	low-spin	$[\pi(d)]^5$	$Fe(CN)_6^{3-}$
	high-spin	$[\pi(d)]^3[\sigma*(d)]^2$	$Mn(H_2O)_6^{2+}$
$3d^6$	low-spin	$[\pi(d)]^6$	$Co(NH_3)_6^{3+}$
	high-spin	$[\pi(d)]^4[\sigma*(d)]^2$	CoF_6^{3-}
$3d^7$	low-spin	$[\pi(d)]^6[\sigma*(d)]$	$Co(NO_2)_6^{4-}$
	high-spin	$[\pi(d)]^5[\sigma*(d)]^2$	$Co(H_2O)_6^{2+}$
$3d^8$		$[\pi(d)]^6[\sigma*(d)]^2$	$Ni(NH_3)_6^{2+}$
$3d^9$		$[\pi(d)]^6[\sigma*(d)]^3$	$Cu(H_2O)_6^{2+}$

The first-row transition-metal ions that form the largest number of stable octahedral complexes are $Cr^{3+}(d^3)$, $Ni^{2+}(d^8)$, and $Co^{3+}(d^6;$ low-spin). This observation is consistent with the fact that the MO configurations $[\pi(d)]^3$ and $[\pi(d)]^6$ take maximum advantage of the more stable $\pi(d)$ level. The $[\pi(d)]^6[\sigma*(d)]^2$ configuration is stable for relatively small Δ values.

The splitting for the tetrahedral geometry is always small, and no low-spin complexes are known for first-row transition-metal ions. There are many stable tetrahedral complexes of $Co^{2+}(3d^7)$, among them $CoCl_4^{2-}$, $Co(NCS)_4^{2-}$, and $Co(OH)_4^{2-}$. This is consistent with the fact that the $[\pi*(d)]^4[\sigma*(d)]^3$ configuration makes maximum use of the more stable $\pi*(d)$ level.

9-14 THE ELECTRONIC SPECTRA OF OCTAHEDRAL COMPLEXES

The $Ti(H_2O)_6^{3+}$ spectrum is simple, since the only d–d transition possible is $\pi(d) \rightarrow \sigma*(d)$. We must now consider how many absorption bands can be expected in complexes containing metal ions with more than one d electron. One simple and useful method is to calculate the splitting of the free-ion terms in an octahedral crystal field. As an example, consider the spectrum of $V(H_2O)_6^{2+}$.

The valence electronic configuration of V^{2+} is $3d^3$. The free-ion terms for d^3 are obtained as outlined in Chapter I; they are ^4F, ^4P, ^2G, ^2D, and ^2S, the ground state being ^4F according to Hund's rules.

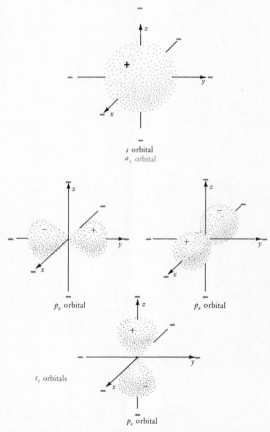

Figure 9-19   Splittings of the s, p, d, and f orbitals in an octahedral crystal field.

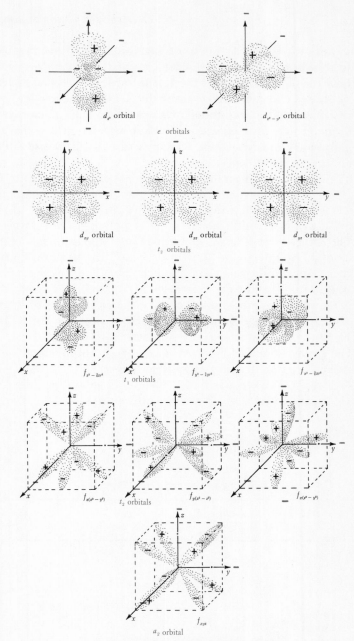

Figure 9-19 (continued)

Since transitions between states that have different S values are forbidden (referred to as spin-forbidden), we shall consider the splitting of only the ^4F and ^4P terms in the octahedral field. In order to determine this splitting, we make use of the fact that the free-ion terms and the single-electron orbitals with the same angular momentum split up into the same number of levels in a crystal field. That is, a D term splits into two levels, which we call T_2 and E, just as the d orbitals split into t_2 and e levels.

The s, p, d, and f orbitals are shown in an octahedral field in Fig. 9–19. The splittings we deduce from Fig. 9–19 are summarized in Table 9–3. We see that the ^4F term splits into three levels, $^4A_2$, $^4T_2$, and $^4T_1$; the ^4P term does not split, but simply gives a $^4T_1$ level.

The energy-level diagram appropriate for a discussion of the spectrum of $V(H_2O)_6^{2+}$ is shown in Fig. 9–20. The ^4P term is placed higher than ^4F, following Hund's second rule. The ^4P term is known to be 11,500 cm^{-1} above the ^4F term in the V^{2+} ion. A calculation is required in order to obtain the relative energies of the three levels produced from the ^4F term. The results are given in Fig. 9–20 in terms of the octahedral splitting parameter Δ.

The ground state of $V(H_2O)_6^{2+}$ is $^4A_2$. From the diagram, we see that there are three transitions possible: $^4A_2 \rightarrow {}^4T_2$; $^4A_2 \rightarrow {}^4T_1(F)$; and $^4A_2 \rightarrow {}^4T_1(P)$. The spectrum of $V(H_2O)_6^{2+}$ is shown in Fig. 9–21. There are three bands, in agreement with the theoretical prediction.

Table 9-3
Splittings Deduced from Figure 9-19

Orbital Set	Number of levels	Level notation	Level degeneracy
s	1	a_1	1
p	1	t_1	3
d	2	t_2	3
		e	2
f	3	a_2	1
		t_2	3
		t_1	3

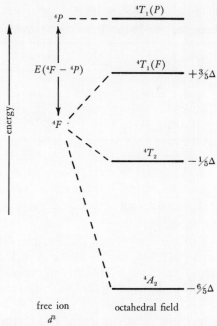

Figure 9–20 Energy-level diagram for a d^3 metal ion in an octahedral field.

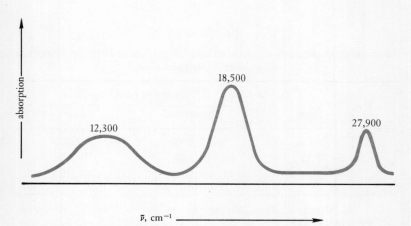

Figure 9–21 Electronic absorption spectrum of $V(H_2O)_6^{+2+}$.

Table 9-4

Energy Expressions for the Three Possible Transitions of $V(H_2O)_6{}^{2+}$

Transition	Energy
${}^4A_2 \rightarrow {}^4T_2$	Δ
${}^4A_2 \rightarrow {}^4T_1(F)$	$\frac{9}{5}\Delta$
${}^4A_2 \rightarrow {}^4T_1(P)$	$\frac{6}{5}\Delta + E({}^4F - {}^4P)$

According to the energy-level diagram, the energies of the transitions are those listed in Table 9–4.

Assigning the first band at 12,300 cm^{-1} to the ${}^4A_2 \rightarrow {}^4T_2$ transition, we obtain $\Delta = 12,300$ cm^{-1}. Using $\Delta = 12,300$ cm^{-1} and $E({}^4F - {}^4P) = 11,500$ cm^{-1} for $V(H_2O)_6{}^{2+}$, the other two transition energies can be calculated and compared with experiment as shown in Table 9–5.

The appropriate energy-level diagrams for several important d electron configurations are given in Fig. 9–22.

Table 9-5

Comparison between Calculated and Observed Transition Energies for $V(H_2O)_6{}^{2+}$

Transition	Energy values, cm^{-1}	
	Calculated	Observed[a]
${}^4A_2 \rightarrow {}^4T_2$	(12,300)	12,300
${}^4A_2 \rightarrow {}^4T_1(F)$	22,140	18,500
${}^4A_2 \rightarrow {}^4T_1(P)$	26,260	27,900

[a]C. K. Jørgensen, *Absorption Spectra and Chemical Bonding*, Pergamon, London, 1962, p. 290.

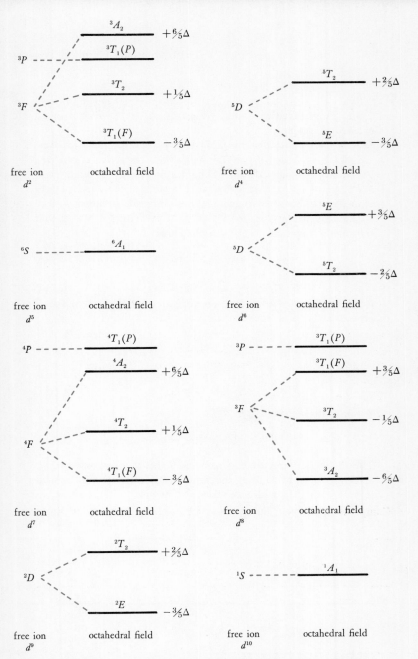

Figure 9-22 Energy-level diagrams for the d^n metal ions in an octahedral field.

207

PROBLEM

9–1. Show that the d_{z^2} and $d_{x^2-y^2}$ orbitals are equivalent in an octahedral complex.

Solution. We shall solve this problem by calculating the total overlap of the $d_{x^2-y^2}$ and d_{z^2} orbitals with their respective normalized ligand-orbital combinations. The total overlap in each case, $S(d_{x^2-y^2})$ and $S(d_{z^2})$, will be expressed in terms of the standard two-atom overlap between d_{z^2} and a ligand σ orbital, as shown in Fig. 9–23. This overlap is called $S(\sigma, d_\sigma)$. From Table 1–1, we see that the angular functions for $d_{x^2-y^2}$ and d_{z^2} are

$$d_{z^2} = c(3z^2 - r^2) \qquad (9\text{--}14)$$

and

$$d_{x^2-y^2} = \sqrt{3}c(x^2 - y^2) \qquad (9\text{--}15)$$

with $c = \sqrt{5}/(4\sqrt{\pi r^2})$. The normalized combinations of ligand orbitals are

$$d_{z^2}: \qquad \frac{1}{2\sqrt{3}}(2z_5 + 2z_6 - z_1 - z_2 - z_3 - z_4) \qquad (9\text{--}16)$$

and

$$d_{x^2-y^2}: \qquad \tfrac{1}{2}(z_1 - z_2 + z_3 - z_4) \qquad (9\text{--}17)$$

We first evaluate $S(d_{x^2-y^2})$:

$$S(d_{x^2-y^2}) = \int \sqrt{3}c(x^2 - y^2)\tfrac{1}{2}(z_1 - z_2 + z_3 - z_4) \; d\tau \qquad (9\text{--}18)$$

This integral is transformed into the standard two-atom overlap integral $S(\sigma, d_\sigma)$ by rotating the metal coordinate system to coincide in turn with the coordinate systems of ligands ①, ②, ③, and ④.

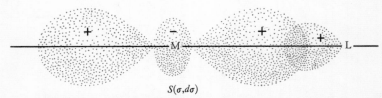

$S(\sigma, d\sigma)$

Figure 9–23   Standard two-atom σ overlap between a d and a ligand σ valence orbital.

Using the coordinates shown in Fig. 9–24, we obtain the following transformations:

M to ①	M to ②	M to ③	M to ④
$z \to y$	$z \to x$	$z \to -x$	$z \to -y$
$x \to -z$	$x \to y$	$x \to z$	$x \to -x$
$y \to x$	$y \to -z$	$y \to -y$	$y \to z$

Thus we have:

$$\frac{\sqrt{3}}{2}c(x^2 - y^2)z_1 \to \frac{\sqrt{3}}{2}c(z^2 - x^2)\sigma \tag{9–19}$$

$$-\frac{\sqrt{3}}{2}c(x^2 - y^2)z_2 \to -\frac{\sqrt{3}}{2}c(y^2 - z^2)\sigma \tag{9–20}$$

$$\frac{\sqrt{3}}{2}c(x^2 - y^2)z_3 \to \frac{\sqrt{3}}{2}c(z^2 - y^2)\sigma \tag{9–21}$$

$$-\frac{\sqrt{3}}{2}c(x^2 - y^2)z_4 \to -\frac{\sqrt{3}}{2}c(x^2 - z^2)\sigma \tag{9–22}$$

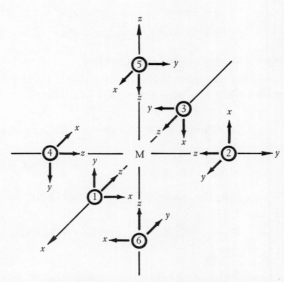

Figure 9–24   Coordinate system for an octahedral complex.

Adding the four transformed terms, we have

$$S(d_{x^2-y^2}) = \int \sqrt{3}c(2z^2 - x^2 - y^2)\sigma \, d\tau = \int \sqrt{3}c(3z^2 - r^2)\sigma \, d\tau$$
$$= \sqrt{3}S(\sigma,d_\sigma) \tag{9-23}$$

Next we evaluate $S(d_{z^2})$:

$$S(d_{z^2}) = \int c(3z^2 - r^2)\frac{1}{2\sqrt{3}}(2z_5 + 2z_6 - z_1 - z_2 - z_3 - z_4) \, d\tau \tag{9-24}$$

The integrals involving z_5 and z_6 are simply two-atom overlaps, as shown in Fig. 9–23. Thus we have

$$\int c(3z^2 - r^2)\frac{1}{2\sqrt{3}}(2z_5 + 2z_6) \, d\tau = \frac{2}{\sqrt{3}}S(\sigma,d_\sigma) \tag{9-25}$$

The integral involving z_1, z_2, z_3, and z_4 is transformed into $S(\sigma,d_\sigma)$, using the transformation table that was used for $S(d_{x^2-y^2})$. Thus

$$-c(3z^2 - r^2)z_1 \rightarrow -c(3y^2 - r^2)\sigma \tag{9-26}$$
$$-c(3z^2 - r^2)z_2 \rightarrow -c(3x^2 - r^2)\sigma \tag{9-27}$$
$$-c(3z^2 - r^2)z_3 \rightarrow -c(3x^2 - r^2)\sigma \tag{9-28}$$
$$-c(3z^2 - r^2)z_4 \rightarrow -c(3y^2 - r^2)\sigma \tag{9-29}$$

Totaling the four transformed terms, we find

$$\int c(3z^2 - r^2)\frac{1}{2\sqrt{3}}(-z_1 - z_2 - z_3 - z_4) \, d\tau$$
$$= \frac{1}{2\sqrt{3}}\int c(6x^2 + 6y^2 - 4r^2)\sigma \, d\tau = \frac{1}{\sqrt{3}}\int c(3z^2 - r^2)\sigma \, d\tau$$
$$= \frac{1}{\sqrt{3}}S(\sigma,d_\sigma) \tag{9-30}$$

Finally, combining the results of Eqs. (9–25) and (9–30), we obtain

$$S(d_{z^2}) = \frac{2}{\sqrt{3}}S(\sigma,d_\sigma) + \frac{1}{\sqrt{3}}S(\sigma,d_\sigma) = \sqrt{3}S(\sigma,d_\sigma) \tag{9-31}$$

Then

$$S(d_{z^2}) = S(d_{x^2-y^2}) = \sqrt{3}S(\sigma,d_\sigma) \tag{9-32}$$

Thus the total overlap of $d_{x^2-y^2}$ and d_{z^2} with properly normalized ligand-orbital combinations is the same, and it follows that the two orbitals are equivalent in an octahedral complex.

SUPPLEMENTARY PROBLEMS

1. Under what conditions are the molecular-orbital and valence-bond descriptions of the σ bonding in an octahedral complex equivalent? Derive the valence-bond functions shown in Fig. 9–7 from the general molecular-orbital functions.

2. Construct the molecular-orbital and valence-bond wave functions for the σ bonding in a square-planar complex. When are the molecular-orbital and valence-bond descriptions the same?

3. Which complex has the larger Δ value, $Co(CN)_6^{3-}$ or $Co(NH_3)_6^{3+}$? $Co(NH_3)_6^{3+}$ or CoF_6^{3-}? $Co(H_2O)_6^{3+}$ or $Rh(H_2O)_6^{3+}$? $PdCl_4^{2-}$ or $PtCl_4^{2-}$? PtI_4^{2-} or $PtCl_4^{2-}$? VCl_4 or $CoCl_4^{2-}$? VCl_4 or CoF_6^{3-}? $PdCl_4^{2-}$ or $RhCl_6^{3-}$? $Co(H_2O)_6^{2+}$ or $Co(H_2O)_6^{3+}$?

4. Give the number of unpaired electrons for each of the following complexes: (*a*) VF_6^{3-}; (*b*) $FeCl_4^-$; (*c*) $NiCl_4^{2-}$ (tetrahedral); (*d*) $PdCl_4^{2-}$; (*e*) $Cu(NH_3)_4^{2+}$; (*f*) $Fe(CN)_6^{4-}$; (*g*) $Fe(CN)_6^{3-}$; (*h*) TiF_6^{3-}; (*i*) $Ni(CN)_4^{2-}$; (*j*) $RhCl_6^{3-}$; (*k*) $IrCl_6^{2-}$.

5. Explain why Zn^{2+} is colorless in aqueous solution. Why is Mn^{2+} pale pink?

6. The spectrum of $Ni(NH_3)_6^{2+}$ shows bands at 10,750, 17,500, and 28,200 cm^{-1}. Calculate the spectrum, using the appropriate diagram in Fig. 9–22 and assuming that $\Delta E(^3F - {}^3P) = 15,800$ cm^{-1} for Ni^{2+}. What are the assignments of the three bands?

7. Plot the energies of the four states arising from ^3F and ^3P in the d^2 octahedral-field case (see Fig. 9–22) for Δ values up to 20,000 cm^{-1}. Assume a reasonable value for $\Delta E(^3F - {}^3P)$. Predict the general features of the absorption spectra expected for d^2 ions in an octahedral field for Δ values of 8,000, 12,000, and 18,000 cm^{-1}.

Suggested Reading

C. J. Ballhausen, *Introduction to Ligand-Field Theory*, McGraw-Hill, New York, 1962. An excellent treatment of electronic structure of transition-metal complexes.

C. J. Ballhausen and H. B. Gray, *Introductory Notes on Molecular-Orbital Theory*, Benjamin, New York, 1965. More advanced than the present treatment.

E. Cartmell and G. W. A. Fowles, *Valency and Molecular Structure*, 2d ed., Butterworths, London, 1961.

F. A. Cotton, *Chemical Applications of Group Theory*, Wiley-Interscience, New York, 1963. The best place for a chemist to go to learn how to use group theory.

C. A. Coulson, *Valence*, 2d ed., Oxford University Press, Oxford, 1961. Thorough treatments of molecular-orbital and valence-bond theories.

H. Eyring, J. Walter, and G. E. Kimball, *Quantum Chemistry*, Wiley, New York, 1960. Highly recommended.

G. Herzberg, *Atomic Spectra and Atomic Structure*, Dover, New York, 1944. Complete and rigorous treatment of the subject matter presented in Chapter I.

J. W. Linnett, *Wave Mechanics and Valency*, Wiley, New York, 1960. Good discussion of diatomic molecules.

L. E. Orgel, *An Introduction to Transition-Element Chemistry: Ligand-Field Theory*, Methuen, London, 1960. Nonmathematical approach.

R. G. Parr, *The Quantum Theory of Molecular Electronic Structure*, Benjamin, New York, 1963. Mathematical treatment of small molecules and organic π orbital systems.

L. Pauling, *The Nature of the Chemical Bond*, Cornell University Press, Ithaca, N.Y., 1960. The classic book on valence-bond theory.

F. O. Rice and E. Teller, *The Structure of Matter*, Wiley, New York, 1949. A very readable account of quantum-mechanical methods.

A Final Message

It is currently popular in elementary courses to discuss chemical bonding as if the subject were completely understood. My opinion is that this approach is very dangerous and should be avoided. In reality, our knowledge of the chemical bond is still at a primitive stage of development. It is fair to admit that the approximate theories at our disposal are able to correlate a large body of experimental information, and that, therefore, we have provided a workable *language* for the "laws" of chemical bonding. However, *the theory* which gives an exact accounting of the forces that hold atoms together and allows an accurate prediction of all the properties of polyatomic molecules is far in the future.

Appendix

Atomic Orbital Ionization Energies

Throughout the book we have presented molecular orbital energy level schemes in a take-it-or-leave-it fashion. To better understand the diagrams in this book, and to construct similar MO energy level schemes, it is desirable to know the relative energies of the combining valence orbitals. The orbital ionization energies which are given in Table A–1 were calculated at Columbia by Dr. Arlen Viste and Mr. Harold Basch. They are the one-electron ionization energies of the valence orbitals in the atoms given, calculated by finding the average energies of both the ground-state and ionized-state configurations (that is, the average energy of all the terms within a particular configuration was calculated).

Table A–1 follows on page 218.

Orbital Ionization Energies

Atom configurations s or $s^2 p^n$; energies in 10^3 cm^{-1}

Atom	$1s$	$2s$	$2p$	$3s$	$3p$	$4s$	$4p$
H	110						
He	198						
Li		44					
Be		75					
B		113	67				
C		157	86				
N		206	106				
O		261	128				
F		374	151				
Ne		391	174				
Na				42			
Mg				62			
Al				91	48		
Si				121	63		
P				151	82		
S				167	94		
Cl				204	111		
Ar				236	128		
K						35	
Ca						49	
Zn						76	
Ga						102	48
Ge						126	61
As						142	73
Se						168	87
Br						194	101
Kr						222	115

Atom	$3d^{n-1}4s \rightarrow 3d^{n-2}4s$ $3d$	$3d^{n-1}4s \rightarrow 3d^{n-1}$ $4s$	$3d^{n-1}4p \rightarrow 3d^{n-1}$ $4p$
Sc	38	46	26
Ti	45	49	27
V	51	51	28
Cr	58	53	28
Mn	64	55	29
Fe	70	57	30
Co	76	59	31
Ni	81	61	31
Cu	86	62	32

Index

Al(CH$_3$)$_3$, 118
Alkali halides, 75
Alkaline-earth halides, 100
Angular momentum, 3, 14
    total, 22
Angular wave function, 14
Atomic number, 22
Atoms, 1
    many-electron, 20
Au^{3+}, 193
Aufbau principle, 20

β, 44
    in C$_2$H$_4$, 164
    in C$_6$H$_6$, 175
B$_2$, 56
Back bonding (donation), 189, 190
Balmer series, 35
B(CH$_3$)$_3$, 118
Be$_2$, 56
BeH$_2$, 87
Bent bonds, 160
    in C$_2$H$_2$, 160
BF$_3$, 106
BN, 80
BO, 81
Bohr orbits, 22, 34
Bohr-Sommerfeld theory, 9

Bohr theory, 1
Bonds, 36
    covalent, 37
    electron pair (Lewis), 37, 39
Bond angle (*see* Bond properties)
Bond energy (*see* Bond properties)
Bond length (*see* Bond properties)
Bond properties, table of diatomic
        molecules, heteronuclear, 82
    homonuclear, 39
    organic molecules, 163
    tetrahedral molecules, 127
    triatomic molecules, angular, 153
        linear, 102
    trigonal planar molecules, 118
    trigonal pyramidal molecules, 138
Br$_2$, 59

C$_2$, 56
CaCl$_2$, 102
Charge densities, 12
    BeH$_2$, 93
    CH$_3$CN, 168
    CH$_4$, 121, 155
    C$_2$H$_2$, 167
    C$_2$H$_4$, 156
    C$_2$H$_6$, 155
    C$_6$H$_6$, 170

219

Cl_2, 59
ClO_4^{2-}, 128
CN, 81
CN^-, 81, 188
CO, 81
CO^+, 81
CO_3^{2-}, 117
Co^{3+}, 201
$CoCl_4^{2-}$, 201
Complementarity principle, 11
$Co(NCS)_4^{2-}$, 201
Configuration interaction, $\sigma(s) - \sigma(p)$, 54, 55, 142
$Co(OH)_4^{2-}$, 201
Coordinate bond energy, 77
Coulomb energy, 45
Coulomb integral, 44, 171
Cr^{3+}, 201
Crystal field theory, 186, 188
    of effect of octahedral field on orbitals, 202
    of octahedral field, 186
Cs_2, 59

Δ, 183, 187
    effect of, back bonding, 199
        charge on metal, 199
        geometry, 197
        interaction of molecular orbitals, 198
        n quantum number, 200
    value of, 196
Diatomic molecules, 36
    heteronuclear, 62
    homonuclear, 36, 49
Diborane, 118
Dipole, 67
    bond, 138, 139, 145
    table of molecular dipoles for diatomic, 70

    triatomic angular, 148
    trigonal pyramidal, 140
Dissociation energy, 100

Eigenfunctions, 13, 14
Eigenvalues, 13
Einstein equation, 9
Electron affinity, 33
Electron diffraction, 11
Electronegativity, 69, 71
Electron spin, 17, 20, 48
Electron waves, 9
Electrostatic energy, 73, 74, 103
    of $CaCl_2$, 103
Energy levels, 42
    BeH_2, 91
    BF_3, 113
    CH_4, 124
    C_2H_2, 168
    C_2H_4, 165
    C_6H_6, 173
    CO_2, 99
    diatomic molecules, heteronuclear, 79
        homonuclear, 54
    H_2, 47
    H_2^+, 45
    H_2CO, 165
    H_2O, 145
    NH_3, 139
    NO_2, 151
    octahedral field, 203, 206
    $PtCl_4^{2-}$, 143
    $Ti(H_2O)_6^{3+}$, 182
    VCl_4, 195
Excited state, atomic, 5

F_2, 57

Ground-state electronic configuration,
  atomic, 5, 20, 26
  molecular, B_2, 56
    Be_2, 56
    BeH_2, 91, 93, 95
    BF_3, 114
    BN, 80
    BO, 81
    Br_2, 59
    C_2, 56
    CH_4, 122
    C_2H_2, 168
    C_2H_4, 159
    C_6H_6, 173
    Cl_2, 59
    CN, 81
    CN^-, 81
    CO, 81
    CO^+, 81
    CO_2, 99
    Cs_2, 58
    F_2, 57
    H_2, 46
    H_2^+, 45
    I_2, 59
    K_2, 58
    Li_2, 55
    LiH, 68
    N_2, 57
    Na_2, 58
    Ne_2, 58
    NH_3, 138
    NO, 81
    NO^+, 81
    NO_2, 152
    O_2, 57
    $PtCl_4^{2-}$, 191
    $Ti(H_2O)_6^{3+}$, 182
    VCl_4, 195
Ground-state term, atomic, 25, 27, 35
  molecular, 60

  H_2, 61
  O_2, 61
Group-theoretical symbols, 187

H_2, 36, 46, 47
H_2^+, 43, 47
Hamiltonian operator, 13
H_2CO, 164
H_2O, 142
Hückel approximation, 171
Hund's rules, 25
Hybridization, d^2sp^3, 184
    sd^3, 194
    sp, 55
      in BeH_2, 93
      in C_2H_2, 167
    sp^2, 115, 116
      in BF_3, 114
      in C_2H_4, 157
      in C_6H_6, 170
      in H_2CO, 164
    sp^3, 126
      bent bonds, 161
      in CH_4, 125, 155
      in C_2H_6, 155
      in H_2CO, 164
      in H_2O, 146
Hydrocarbons, 155

I_2, 59
Interelectronic repulsion, 59, 135
    in H_2O, 144
    in NH_3, 135
Internuclear distance, 37
Ionic bonding, 73
    in alkalai halides, 75
    in LiH, 68
    in triatomic molecules, 100

Ionic resonance energy, 71
Ionization potentials, 6, 7, 27, 32, 44
   orbital, 215

K_2, 59
Kekulé structure, 174

$L - S$ terms, 22
Li_2, 55
Ligands, 176
LiH, 62
Linear combination of atomic orbit-
   als, 38
London energy, 75
Lyman series, 8

Magnetic properties, 200
   diamagnetism, 48, 191
   high-spin complexes, 200
   low-spin complexes, 200
   magnetic moment, 48
   paramagnetism, 48, 183
   strong-field ligands, 200
   weak-field ligands, 200
Microstates, 23
Molecular orbitals, antibonding, 39
   BeH_2, 90
   BF_3, 107
   bonding, 39
   CH_4, 121
   C_2H_2, 167
   C_2H_4, 157, 159
   C_6H_6, 170
   CO_2, 98
   coefficients, 66
      of BeH_2, 89, 92
   degenerate, 55

H_2, 45
H_2^+, 43
H_2CO, 164
H_2O, 142, 146
LiH, 65
NH_3, 129
NO_2, 148
octahedral complexes, 178
π, 50
   ligand-to-metal π bonding, 188,
      190
   metal-to-ligand π bonding, 189
σ orbitals, 49, 53
square-planar, 190
tetrahedral, 194
Molecular orbital theory, 38

N_2, 57
N_2^+, 57
Na_2, 59
Ne_2, 58
NH_3, 129
Ni^{2+}, 193, 201
NO, 81
NO^+, 81
NO_2, 148
NO_3^-, 117
Node, 16
Normalization, 13
Nuclear charge, effective, 33

O_2, 57
Octahedral complexes, 186
Orbitals, 14, 16, 20, 21
   d, 14, 18, 176
   f, 14, 18
   p, 14, 17
   s, 14, 16
   valence, 39

Organic molecules, 125, 155
Overlap, 40, 42
  of orbitals in, BeH_2, 88
    BF_3, 108 ff.
    CH_4, 122, 123
    CO_2, 97
    H_2O, 143, 144
    LiH, 63
    NH_3, 131 ff.
    octahedral complexes, 184
    square-planar complexes, 192
    $Ti(H_2O)_6^{3+}$, 179, 180
  standard two-atom, d-σ, 207
    p-$p(\pi)$, 51
    p-$p(\sigma)$, 50, 114
    s-p, 133
    s-s, 50

Pauli principle, 20
Pd^{2+}, 193
Photons, 9, 10
Planck's constant, 5
Pt^{2+}, 193
$PtCl_4^{2-}$, 189

Quantum assumption, 3
Quantum jump, 5
Quantum number, l, 14, 20, 22
  m_l, 14, 20, 22
  m_s, 14, 20, 22
  n, 4, 14, 20

Radial wave function, 13
Rb_2, 59

Square-planar complexes, 189

Term designation, 23
Term symbols, for linear molecules, 60
Tetrahedral metal complexes, 194
Tetrahedral molecules, 121, 137, 155
$Ti(H_2O)_6^{3+}$, 176
Transition metals, 176
Triatomic molecules, angular, 142
  linear, 87
Trigonal planar molecules, 106
Trigonal pyramidal molecules, 130

Uncertainty principle, 11, 12

Valence-bond theory, BeH_2, 93, 95
  BF_3, 115, 117
  CH_4, 125, 126
  CH_3CN, 164
  C_2H_2, 164
  C_2H_4, 159
  C_2H_6, 155
  C_6H_6, 174
  CO_2, 100
  H_2CO, 166
  H_2O, 146
  NH_3, 137
  NO_2, 152
  octahedral complexes, 187, 182
  $Ti(H_2O)_6^{3+}$, 184, 185
van der Waals energy, 73, 103
VCl_4, 194
$V(H_2O)_6^{2+}$, 202

Wave function, 12, 13
  angular, 14
  radial, 13

Zeeman effect, 9